Student Companion and Problems Book to accompany

Biochemistry

By Campbell

William M. Scovell

Bowling Green State University

Saunders Golden Sunburst Series

Saunders College Publishing

Philadelphia
Fort Worth
Chicago
San Francisco
Montreal
Toronto
Tokyo
Sydney

Copyright ©1991 by Saunders College Publishing, a division of Holt, Rinehart and
Winston.

All rights reserved. No part of this publication may be reproduced or transmitted in
any form or by any means, electronic or mechanical, including photocopy, recording or
any information storage and retrieval system, without permission in writing from the
publisher.

Requests for permission to make copies of any part of the work should be mailed to:
Permissions, Holt, Rinehart and Winston, Inc., Orlando, Florida 32887.

Printed in the United States of America.

Campbell: Student Companion and Problems Book to accompany BIOCHEMISTRY

ISBN # 0-03-073572-6

123 002 987654321

PREFACE

I hear, and I forget
I see, and I remember
I do, and I understand

"Ancient Chinese Proverb"

The study of and understanding of biochemistry is one of the most daunting, yet stimulating experiences in the chemistry-biology curriculum. It draws on your comprehension of many aspects of fundamental chemistry, introduces new concepts and techniques associated with biochemistry and integrates them into a basic understanding of the activities of a living cell. The intellectual challenge is apparent. As with any new undertaking, however, one must decide on a strategy to accomplish the objectives before you. At the same time, it is beneficial to have some "marker" to evaluate your progress and the extent to which you have accomplished the original goals.

It is with this in mind that <u>The Student Companion and Problems Book</u> was written. It is to accompany and complement the text, with the objective of helping the student gain a more comprehensive understanding of biochemistry.

Each chapter starts with an overview which highlights the ideas and concepts presented in the corresponding chapter in <u>Biochemistry</u> by M. K. Campbell. The Chapter Objectives focus attention on specific concepts, techniques, procedures and approaches to problem solving that are important to assimilating the material.

The major emphasis of the book is in the collection of additional problems, which is accompanied by detailed explanations and answers. It is important that these problems be solved or seriously attempted by the student before the answers are consulted. A major effort and commitment at this point in the learning process pays huge dividends in reinforcing and crystallizing your knowledge.

A Review of Important Organic Reactions in Biochemistry has been included in Chapter 4. This section will emphasize that biochemistry is clearly "the chemistry of living systems" and that these reactions provide the foundation for the anabolic and catabolic reactions in cellular metabolism.

In addition, a number of important topics that are currently experiencing rapid, if not explosive, development are "SPOTLIGHTED" in this Student Companion. These are found in appropriate chapters and serve to point out the impact that these developments have on today's burgeoning understanding of the molecular basis of biology.

I would like to acknowledge Dr. Susan G. Cady and Dr. Ronald C. Peterson for their scientific reviews of this text.

I welcome comments from students and professors, especially those which bring any errors in the text to my attention.

Comments should be addressed to:

Professor William M. Scovell
Department of Chemistry
Overman Hall
Bowling Green State University
Bowling Green, OH 43403

TABLE OF CONTENTS

Chapter	Title	Page

Part I   The Position Of Biochemistry In The Sciences

1   The Context of Biochemistry   1

2   The Organization of Cells   4

3   Water, Hydrogen Bonding, pH and Buffers   9

Part II   The Molecular Nature Of Cellular Components

4   The Molecules of Life   22

5   Amino Acids and Peptides   38

6   Carbohydrates   48

7   Lipids   60
       SPOTLIGHT:
          Controversial Drugs: Synthetic Steroids

Part III   The Dynamic Aspects Of Biochemical Reactions

8   Energy Requirements For Life-Thermodynamics   72

9   The Three-Dimensional Structure of Proteins   81

10   The Behavior of Proteins-Enzymes   92

11   The Dynamics of Membrane Structure   101

Part IV   **Metabolism**

12   Metabolism and Electron Transfer   113

13   Glycolysis-Anaerobic Oxidation of Glucose   122

14   The Citric Acid Cycle   132

15   Electron Transport and Oxidative Phosphorylation   142

16   Lipid Metabolism   153
     SPOTLIGHT:
        Atherosclerosis: Cholesterol and the LDL Connection

17   Photosynthesis   167

18   The Metabolism of Nitrogen   178

19   Summary of Metabolism   191

Part V   **The Workings Of The Genetic Code**

20   The Structure of Nucleic Acids   202
     SPOTLIGHT:
        DNA in Court: "Molecular Fingerprint" Evidence

21   Biosynthesis of Nucleic Acids   221
     SPOTLIGHT:
        RNA as an Enzyme: The Changing of a Mind-Set

22   The Biosynthesis of Proteins   232
     SPOTLIGHT:
        Cystic Fibrosis: The Gene, The Protein and Possible
        Gene Therapy

The Context of Biochemistry

This first chapter presents some of the most significant tenets which provide the basis for understanding the chemistry in biological systems - biochemistry. These "grand statements" also highlight the unifying principles which will be developed in more detail in the subsequent chapters. In addition, this chapter explores possible routes by which life began. Since living organisms are made up of and powered by lifeless molecules that were originally thought to have formed under anaerobic conditions. Questions are raised regarding the origin and character of the earth, the molecules first formed, the importance of photosynthesis and the subsequent development of aerobic organisms.

CHAPTER OBJECTIVES

1.   Distinguish between the general meanings for the term "oxidation" and how these different statements might be used in anaerobic and aerobic processes.
2.   Describe two model systems for biomolecules and cells and indicate their importance in understanding the development of biomacromolecules and living cells.

3. Discuss the theories regarding the origin of life, with specific attention to the molecules thought to be the first molecules formed.

4. Discuss the importance of photosynthetic processes which began to utilize water as a reducing agent and the effect of the resulting products on life today.

5. Discuss the role of oxidation and reduction processes and ATP production in catabolic and anabolic metabolic processes.

EXERCISES

1. The early atmosphere on earth is thought to be _____ in character, with little or no free _____ .

2. Two common features of living organisms are:

_____

_____

3. The most abundant element in the universe is _____ , while the two most abundant elements in living organisms are _____ and _____ . In both the universe and in living systems, the non-metallic elements, H, C, N and O, are in _____ abundance.

4. The _____ and _____ are the two classes of organic bases found in nucleic acids. However, the repeating monomeric unit found in the (polymeric) nucleic acids is a _____.

5. Oxidative reactions of ingested nutrients are important in _____ (metabolic) processes and can be regarded as either the loss of _____ or the gain of _____ .

6. Reactions involving reductions, which are associated with _____ (metabolic) processes, can be regarded likewise as either the gain of _____ or the loss of _____ .

7. Photosynthesis can be conveniently considered as two complex reactions. The first one is associated with the _____ and is referred to as the light reaction, while the second reaction, referred to as the _____ reaction, is associated with the reduction of _____ to produce _____. An important product of the first reaction, which is used in the subsequent reaction, is _____.

8. Photosynthesis in green plants involves the reaction of water and carbon dioxide to produce carbohydrate (use $C_6H_{12}O_6$) and molecular oxygen. Write the balanced equation for this reaction.

ANSWERS TO EXERCISES

1. reducing, oxygen (O_2).
2. All living organisms (1) use energy and (2) make use of the same types of biomolecules.
3. H, C, O; high.
4. purines, pyrimidines; nucleotide.
5. catabolic, electrons, oxygen.
6. anabolic, electrons, oxygen.
7. the capture of light energy, dark, CO_2, carbohydrates; ATP.
8. $$6\ H_2O + 6\ CO_{2(g)} \xrightarrow{h\nu} C_6H_{12}O_6 + 6\ O_{2(g)}$$

2

The Organization of Cells

Living cells can be classified as prokaryotes or eukaryotes. The more complex eukaryotic cells contain a nucleus and other organelles, while prokaryotic cells lack these subcellular compartments. The different types of organelles, all of which are enveloped by a membrane, provide compartments for specialized metabolic activities, such as the oxidation of ingested foods, replication of DNA, and photosynthesis. Examples of the symbiotic behavior between organisms are presented and the possible basis for the origin of eukaryotic cells is discussed.

CHAPTER OBJECTIVES

1. State the characteristics which define a prokaryotic and a eukaryotic cell.
2. Define what constitutes an organelle and specify the functions of the organelles found in a human cell.
3. Indicate the difference between a cell membrane and a cell wall.

4.   Describe the relationship between flagella, undulipodia, pili and cilia.

5.   Characterize the structural components and the function of mitochondria.

6.   Describe the two forms of the endoplasmic reticulum and their location within the cell.

7.   Name the five classes of biological organisms and give an example of each.

8.   Discuss mutualism and parasitic symbiosis and present an example of each.

9.   Discuss the endosymbiotic theory and suggest how it may provide the basis for the origin of eukaryotes.

EXERCISES

1.   a.   What are the molecular components of a cell membrane and a cell wall?

      b.   Are cell membranes and cell walls found in prokaryotic and eukaryotic cells?

      c.   What is the function of the cell wall and the membrane?

2.   Name several organelles found in plants, but not in animal cells. Indicate their function.

3.   How do peroxisomes differ from lysosomes?

4.   How does the DNA in bacterial cells differ from the DNA in human cells?

5.   List the names of the five major classifications for all organisms. Cite an example of each organism. State any unique characteristics of each class and the important features common among some or all the classes.

6. Recently it has become possible to take miniscule amounts of DNA and, by a powerful new procedure called the Polymerase Chain Reaction (PCR), make millions of copies of this DNA fragment very efficiently and without laborious cloning procedures. The procedure, however, requires repeated changes in temperature ranging from 20-80°C. The enzyme used in this procedure is the DNA polymerase isolated from the bacterium, *Thermus aquaticus* (Taq), which lives in hot springs at temperatures of 70-80°C.

     a.   What type of bacterium is the source of this polymerase?

     b.   Suggest a reason why this particular enzyme is so useful.

7. Indicate which of the following statements is true or false. If the statement is false, correct it.

     a.   Ribosomes always reside in the nucleus.

     b.   The mitochondria are organelles in eukaryotic cells which are actively engaged in reductive processes.

     c.   Chloroplasts, glyoxysomes and mitochondria contain DNA.

     d.   Methanogens are aerobic bacteria which produce methane from CO_2 and H_2.

     e.   The mitochondrial proteins are all derived from the genes of mitochondrial DNA.

     f.   There is clear and convincing evidence that eukaryotic cells arose from a symbiotic relationship of prokaryotic cells.

     g.   The undulipodia of prokaryotic cells are primarily made up of the protein tubulin.

     h.   The Golgi apparatus is involved in the secretion of proteins from the cell.

ANSWERS TO EXERCISES

1.   a. Cell membranes are composed of proteins in a double layer (bilayer) of phospholipids. Cell walls consist primarily of polysaccharides.

      b. Both prokaryotic and eukaryotic cells have outer membranes enveloping the cell. Eukaryotic cells also have organelles within the cell which are enclosed by membranes. Prokaryotic cells and plant cells have cell walls, which animal cells do not have.

      c. Cell walls are quite rigid and serve as a protective coating for the cell. The membrane serves as a selective barrier to the intake or release of molecules. In addition, protein molecules that are embedded in the membrane can be involved in intercellular recognition.

2.   Green plants have chloroplasts which contain the apparatus for photosynthesis. Plants also contain glyoxysomes, which have enzymes used in the glyoxylate cycle. This pathway permits the conversion of lipids to carbohydrates.

3.   Peroxisomes are primarily involved with the metabolism (elimination) of toxic hydrogen peroxide, H_2O_2. Lysosomes are sacs of degradative enzymes that are capable of digesting nucleic acids, proteins and lipids.

4.   In bacteria, the DNA is a single, circular molecule which contains the genetic information. It is generally dispersed throughout the cytoplasm, although the DNA is localized to some extent in the nuclear region.

      In human cells, the DNA resides in the nucleus. The DNA is complexed with nuclear proteins to form chromatin, or individual chromosomes (each chromosome is considered to contain a single molecule of DNA) which are observable under the light or electron microscope. The amount of DNA in a human cell is about 1000 times greater than that found in a bacterial cell.

5. The classes are:
      1. Monera   prokaryotic (bacteria)
      2. Protista   unicellular (Paramecium)
      3. Fungi   molds or mushrooms
      4. Plantae   flowers
      5. Animalia   human beings

Class 1 contains only prokaryotic organisms, while the other four classes contain eukaryotic organisms. The Protista class contains primarily unicellular eukaryotic cells, while classes 3-5 are virtually all multicellular. Organisms in the Animalia class do not have cell walls, while those in the Plantae class do have cell walls. **All** organisms are composed of living cells which must metabolize exogenous nutrients to produce energy and to provide molecules for sustained life.

6. a. The polymerase is derived from an archaebacteria called thermacidophile.

 b. The *Thermus aquaticus* bacteria are very hardy in that they survive normally at high temperatures and in some cases, at low pH. This means that their enzymes remain active and stable under these conditions, which would be especially harsh and generally lethal to most other organisms. The DNA polymerase in *Thermus aquaticus* is very stable and active at high temperatures, while DNA polymerases from virtually all other organisms would not function if heated to these extreme temperatures. Therefore, the PCR procedure is carried out with Taq DNA polymerase because it remains active throughout the entire cyclic procedure, especially as high temperatures are encountered.

7.

 a. False.   Ribosomes reside in the cytoplasm.
 b. False.   Mitochondria are actively engaged in oxidative metabolic processes.
 c. False.   Chloroplasts and mitochondria contain DNA. Glyoxysomes do not contain DNA.
 d. False.   Methanogens are anaerobic organisms.
 e. False.   Some mitochondrial proteins are the products of nuclear genes.
 f. False.   The evidence is not convincing.
 g. False.   Undulipodia are flagella in eukaryotes.
 h. True.

3

Water, Hydrogen Bonding, pH and Buffers

The presence of water on earth and its unique characteristics provide the essential basis for life. Its bent structure, polar bonds and capacity to form intermolecular hydrogen bonds make water a high boiling solvent capable of dissolving ions and polar molecules. While compounds which can form hydrogen bonds with water are especially soluble, non-polar or hydrophobic molecules are not soluble. Acids and bases dissolve in water and dissociate either completely (strong acids and bases) or to a small extent (weak acids and bases). The acidity or pH of an aqueous solution is determined by the concentration of protons $[H^+]$ in solution ($pH = -log[H^+]$). Buffers are solutions which contain a weak acid and its conjugate base or a weak base and its conjugate acid, in which the pH is equal to or close to the pK value ($pK_a' = -logK_a'$) for the acid or base. The Henderson-Hasselbalch equation ($pH = pK_a' + log[A^-]/[HA]$) can be readily used to calculate the pH of a weak acid or base or a buffered solution.

CHAPTER OBJECTIVES

1. Describe the concept of electronegativity and explain its role in determining whether a bond is polar or non-polar.

2. Explain how ion-dipole and dipole-dipole interactions between dissolved ions or molecules in water aid in their solubility.

3. Define the terms hydrophilic and hydrophobic and discuss how the preferential interactions of molecules with water or with each other explains their solubility or insolubility.

4. Draw the general structure for a micelle and explain what the driving force is for micelle formation.

5. Indicate the characteristics a molecule must possess to be a hydrogen bond donor or acceptor.

6. Become familiar with the types of non-covalent bonding forces and the magnitude of the energies in the interactions.

7. State the relationship between the strength of an acid and its K_a' and pK_a' values.

8. Review the relationship between the pH of a solution and its hydrogen ion concentration.

9. Make a plot for the titration of a weak acid and indicate the species that are present at the beginning, the half-way point and at the equivalence point in the titration.

10. Define the terms buffer and buffer capacity and explain how the buffering capacity changes as a function of pH.

11. Give some examples of buffers and indicate the buffer species that will react with any added acid or base.

EXERCISES

1. Predict the relative solubility of the following series of molecules in water. Briefly explain your answer.

    a. CH_3COOH, $CH_3(CH_2)_6COOH$, CH_3CH_2COOH

    b.   R-CHO, R-C-R, R-R, R-COOH, R-O-R, in which R = CH_3
                            $\parallel$
                            O

2. Explain how the solubility of these molecules will be affected by pH.

    a.   anilinium cation $pK_a = 4.70$

    b.   formic acid $pK_a = 3.75$

    c.   methylacetate   no pK_a value

need a chemical structure – students don't know

3. Consider the boiling points for the following molecules, all of which have essentially the same molecular weight. Explain the trend in the boiling points in terms of intermolecular hydrogen bonding.

Molecule	Boiling point (^0C)
CH_4 (methane)	-161
NH_3 (ammonia)	-34.5
HF (hydrogen fluoride)	19.4
OH_2 (water)	100

4. Consider the molecules listed below and fill in the table concerned with the characteristics of the individual bonds and of the molecule as a whole. Indicate whether the bond and the molecule is polar or non-polar.

Molecule	Bond(s)	Molecule
OH_2	_____	_____
CH_4	_____	_____
CO_2	_____	_____
BF_3	_____	_____

5. a. Indicate whether the molecules listed below are amphiphilic, hydrophilic or hydrophobic.
   b. Define and characterize a micelle?
   c. Indicate which of these molecules can form micelles in an aqueous solution?

Molecule	Character	Micelle Formation(yes/no)
sodium acetate	_____	_____
normal hexane	_____	_____
potassium salt of octanoic acid	_____	_____
napthalene	_____	_____
SDS (sodium dodecylsulfate)	_____	_____

6. Which of the following molecules interact with each other by hydrogen bonding? For the cases in which this occurs, draw the structure showing the proposed intermolecular interactions.

$$\text{O}$$
$$||$$
a. CH_3CCH_3 and CH_3OH

$$\text{O}$$
$$||$$
b. Urea, H_2NCNH_2 and $CH_3CH_2COCH_3$

$$\text{O}$$
$$||$$
c. CH_3CH_2CH with itself.

d. CH_3Cl and NH_3

e. $N(CH_3)_4^+$ and CH_3COOH

(7.) Non-covalent interactions are important in determining the ultimate structure of important biomacromolecules, such as proteins and nucleic acids. Specify the amount of energy (kJ/mol) associated with the following non-covalent interactions.

Hydrogen bonding   _____

van der Waals bonds   _____

Hydrophobic interactions   _____

(8.) Calculate the pH of the following solutions.

a.   0.1M pyruvic acid; pK_a = 2.50
b.   0.1M lactic acid and 0.1M sodium lactate; pK_a = 3.86
c.   An aqueous solution containing $2.5 \times 10^{-8}M$ OH^-.
d.   A 0.1M succinic acid (pK_{a1} = 4.21; pK_{a2} = 5.63) solution after 0.09 equivalents of NaOH is added.
e.   Which of these solutions would serve as an effective buffer?

[lactic acid]

(9.) Indicate the conjugate acid and/or base for the following species in aqueous solution.

Molecule	Conjugate base	Conjugate acid
a. H_2O		
b. benzoic acid		
c. NH_3		
d. HCO_3^-		
e. $H_2PO_4^-$		

$2 \; H_2O \rightleftharpoons H_3O^+ + OH^-$
acid &   conj   conj
base   acid   base

$H_2O + B-H \rightleftharpoons B^{\ominus} + H_3O^+$
base   acid   conj base   conj acid.

$NH_3 + H_2O \rightleftharpoons NH_4^+ + OH^-$
base   acid   conj acid   conj base

$HCO_3^- + H_2O \rightleftharpoons CO_3^{-2} + H_3O^+$
acid   base   conj base   conj acid

$HCO_3^- + H_2O \rightleftharpoons H_2CO_3 + OH^-$
base   acid   conj acid   conj base

$H_2PO_4^- + H_2O \rightleftharpoons HPO_4^{-2} + H_3O^+$
acid   base   conj base   conj acid.

$H_2PO_4^- + H_2O \rightleftharpoons H_3PO_4 + OH^-$
base   acid   conj acid   conj base

13

10. Stomach acid is thought to be primarily concentrated hydrochloric acid (HCl). If 30.0 mL of 0.10M NaOH is required to neutralize a 50.0 mL sample of stomach acid, calculate the pH of the sample. confusing

11. A 0.1 M Tris buffer [tris(hydroxymethyl)aminomethane; pK = 8.1] is adjusted to pH 8.1 and is used as the buffer solution to study an enzymatic reaction which produces 0.01 moles/L of H^+.

   a. What is the initial ratio of [Tris]/[TrisH+]?

   b. Calculate the initial concentration of the $TrisH^+$ and Tris species?

   c. Calculate the concentrations of Tris and $TrisH^+$ after the reaction?

   d. Calculate the final pH of the solution.

   e. Determine the final pH of the solution if the enzymatic reaction were carried out in 1 L of water, pH = 7, with no buffer present.

12. a. Draw a micelle and point out the hydrophobic region and the charged hydrophilic ends.
   b. Briefly explain the driving force for the formation of a micelle in an aqueous solution.

ANSWERS TO EXERCISES

1.   a. $CH_3COOH > CH_3CH_2COOH > CH_3(CH_2)_6COOH$

These three molecules are simple carboxylic acids. Therefore, the relative solubility will decrease as the molecular weight increases. The decreased solubility corresponds to the increase in the molecular weight of the organic (R) group in the acids.

b. These molecules have approximately the same molecular weight and therefore, the solubility will depend on the extent to which each interacts favorably with water. The extent to which intermolecular hydrogen bonding takes place between the molecule and water is:

$$\text{R-R} < \text{R-O-R} < \text{R-CHO} < \underset{\underset{O}{\|}}{\text{R-C-R}} < \text{R-COOH}$$

Therefore, the solubility also increases in this order.

2. a. The anilinium cation is the protonated form of aniline (pK_a = 4.7). The cation will interact favorably with water and therefore the solubility (of the cation) will increase as the pH is progressively decreased below ca. pH 5. At pH 4.7, there will be equal concentrations of the protonated (soluble) and the unprotonated aniline (relatively insoluble). As the pH is lowered further, there will be increasing amounts of the protonated, soluble form.
   b. The anion of formic acid, $H\text{-}CO_2^-$, will be more soluble than the neutral acid, H-COOH. With a pK_a value of 3.75, its solubility will increase as the pH increases.
   c. This is an ester, which is neither acidic nor basic. Therefore, assuming no reaction, the solubility will be independent of the solution pH. Recall, however, that an ester can be hydrolyzed in strongly basic or acidic solutions.

3. The boiling points for a series of molecules is an indication of the extent of **inter**molecular interactions between the molecules. The trend in the boiling points can be explained by the **type** and the **number** of intermolecular interactions between the molecules.
   Although all the molecules have weak van der Waals interactions between them, the primary effect on the boiling points and other physical characteristics is the extent of intermolecular hydrogen bonding. CH_4 is not capable of hydrogen bonding. HF can donate 1 hydrogen bond and although it has three lone pairs of electrons, it cannot accept three hydrogen bonds. The strength of the one hydrogen bond in HF is, however, very strong. Each H_2O molecule can accept 2 hydrogen bonds and accept 2 hydrogen bonds. This is the optimum hydrogen bonding capacity, with the number of

1 5

hydrogen bond donors equivalent to the number of hydrogen bond acceptors. NH_3 has three hydrogens which can, in principle, take part in hydrogen bonding, but as with HF, this does not occur. Ammonia is limited to only one intermolecular hydrogen bond. The hydrogen bonds in ammonia are not as strong as in water or hydrogen fluoride because of the smaller difference in the electronegativity value in a (N-H) bond than in a (O-H) or (H-F) bond. One of the key points in explaining the high boiling point for H_2O relative to HF and NH_3, therefore, is that only in water can an extensive hydrogen bonding network occur to optimize intermolecular interactions. This is illustrated in Figure 3.6 in the text.

4.

Molecule	Bond(s)	Molecule
OH_2	polar	polar(bent)
CH_4	non-polar	non-polar (tetrahedral)
CO_2	polar	non-polar (linear)
BF_3	polar	non-polar (trigonal planar)

5.   a. and c.

Molecule	Character	Micelle Formation(yes/no)
sodium acetate	hydrophilic	no
normal hexane	hydrophobic	no
potassium salt of octanoic acid	amphiphilic	yes
napthalene	hydrophobic	no
SDS (sodium dodecylsulfate)	amphiphilic	yes

16

b.   A micelle is a globular structure formed by the association of amphiphilic molecules in which the hydrophobic segments reside on the inside of the spherical micelle, while the polar or hydrophilic segments interact with the water on the outer surface of the structure. See Figure 3.3b in the text.

6.   a.   yes.

CH3-C-CH3
$\quad\quad$ ||
$\quad\quad$ O..........H-O-CH3

b.   yes.

c.   Aldehydes do not hydrogen bond with each other since there are no hydrogen bond donors.

d.   NH3 can act as a hydrogen bond donor and acceptor, but CH3Cl cannot hydrogen bond in any way. There will be no hydrogen bonding interactions between these molecules.

e.   Tetramethylammonium cation does not take part in hydrogen bonding. Therefore, there can be no intermolecular hydrogen bonding between this cation and acetic acid, CH3COOH.

7.

Hydrogen bonding	ca. 20 kJ/mol
van der Waals bonds	ca. 4 kJ/mol
Hydrophobic interactions	4-12 kJ/mol

8. a. Pyruvic acid = PyH

$PyH = Py^- + H^+$ $pK_a = 2.50$

$K_a = 3 \times 10^{-3} = [Py^-][H^+]/[PyH]$

$3 \times 10^{-3} = x^2/(0.1- x)$
$x = 1.76 \times 10^{-2}M = [Py^-] = [H^+]$.
$pH = - \log [H^+] = - \log (1.76 \times 10^{-2})$

pH = 1.76

b. Lactic acid = LacH

$LacH = Lac^- + H^+$ $pK = 3.86$

Using the Henderson-Hasselbalch equation,

$pH = pK + \log[Lac^-]/[LacH]$
$= 3.86 + \log(0.1)/(0.1) = 3.86 + \log(1); \log 1 = 0$

pH = 3.86

c.
$[H^+] \times [OH^-] = 1.0 \times 10^{-14}$
If $[OH^-] = 2.5 \times 10^{-8}M$, $[H^+] = 4.0 \times 10^{-7}M$

pH = 6.40

d.   Use the Henderson-Hasselbalch equation and consider only the first pK_a. The 0.09 equivalents of NaOH converts 90% of the H_2Succ to the $HSucc^-$ form, leaving only 10% of the original H_2Succ.

pH = pK + log $[HSucc^-]/[H_2Succ]$
pH = 4.21 + log (0.9/0.1)   = 4.21 + log 9
pH = 4.21 + 0.95

<u>pH = 5.16</u>

e.   The only solution which could effectively serve as a buffer is the lactic acid/lactate solution because there are equivalent concentrations of both the acid and its conjugate base.

9.

	Molecule	Conjugate base	Conjugate acid
a.	H_2O	OH^-	H_3O^+
b.	benzoic acid	benzoate anion	H_3O^+ ~~none~~
c.	NH_3	NH_2^-	NH_4^+
d.	HCO_3^-	CO_3^{-2}	H_2CO_3
e.	$H_2PO_4^-$	HPO_4^{-2}	H_3PO_4

not how I would answer this question

10. $(V_a)(M_a) = (V_b)(M_b)$
(30.0 mL) (0.10M) = (50.0 mL) (x M HCl)
Molarity of HCl = 0.06 M
pH = - log $[H^+]$ = - log (6.0 x 10^{-2} M) = 2.00 - 0.78

<u>pH = 1.22</u> for the stomach acid

11. a.   The solution pH in this problem is equal to the pK_a value for Tris. Therefore, the ratio of [Tris]/[TrisH+] is 1.0.

b.   Since the total buffer concentration is 0.1M and there is equal concentrations of both the Tris and TrisH+ species, the initial concentration of each species is 0.05 M.

c.   The reaction produces 0.01 M H+. The Tris will react with the H+ to increase the concentration of TrisH+ by 0.01 M and decrease the concentration of Tris by 0.01 M.
The concentrations will be:
[TrisH+] = 0.05 + 0.01   = 0.06 M
[Tris]   = 0.05 - 0.01   = 0.04 M

d.   The final pH is calculated with the Henderson-Hasselbalch equation.
pH = 8.1 + log(0.04 M/0.06 M)
pH = 7.92

e.   If 0.01 moles/L of hydrogen ion were added to water at pH = 7, the concentration of H+ would be 0.01M. The pH of a solution with 1.0×10^{-2} M H+ is 2. The comparison of the pH values in answers (d) and (e) exemplifies the role of a buffer solution in maintaining the desired pH when carrying out a reaction which produces acid or base.

12. a.

Hydrophobic
Interior

Hydrophilic, Charged
Exterior

b. The primary driving force for the formation of a micelle is for the hydrophobic segments of the molecules to associate with each other (a favorable interaction) and in the process, not interfere with the structure of water. At the same time, the charged ends point out into the aqueous solution and interact favorably with the water molecules.

4

The Molecules of Life

This chapter serves as a review of important aspects of organic chemistry which provide the foundation for biochemistry. The functional groups in the organic molecules determine the observed chemical reactivity. The amino acids, monosaccharides and nucleotides, which serve as the fundamental building blocks for biomacromolecules such as proteins, polysaccharides and nucleic acids, respectively, are highlighted in this chapter. A preview of the structures of a few lipid molecules is also presented. Important organic reactions which will be relevant in subsequent chapters are also summarized here.

CHAPTER OBJECTIVES

1.   Review the functional groups in organic molecules, be able to recognize them in complex molecules and know the reactions associated with each functional group.

2.   Know the general formula for the α-amino acids and the Greek letter nomenclature indicating the position of a specific carbon atom in a chain.

3.   Be able to recognize the chemical structure for the open and the ring forms of a carbohydrate and distinguish between an aldose and a ketose.

4.   Draw the structures for the two purine and three pyrimidine bases found in nucleic acids and distinguish the difference between a nucleoside and a nucleotide.

5.   Be able to recognize common lipids such as saturated and unsaturated fatty acids, cholesterol and esters formed from glycerol and fatty acids.

ADDITIONAL TOPIC:

A REVIEW OF
IMPORTANT ORGANIC REACTIONS IN BIOCHEMISTRY

The "heart and soul" of biochemistry lies in the metabolic processes actively taking place in living cells. These reactions are associated with the enzymatic interconversion of organic molecules. The ability to recognize the organic functional groups in complex molecules and the chemical reactivity associated with each molecule will serve as a basis for understanding these processes.

The following summary provides a list of general reaction types which will appear in subsequent chapters in the text. The examples are taken directly from organic chemistry. Since these reactions are carried out in non-living systems, they often involve the use of a strong acid or base or the addition of heat to drive the reaction to completion. These same types of reactions found in biological systems are catalyzed by cellular enzymes. The reactions are cataloged according to the functional group.

1. Alkenes (Olefins)   (>C = C<)

Hydration- (addition of water to alkenes to produce an alcohol)

$$-C = C- \ + \ H_2O \ \xrightarrow{H^+} \ -\overset{\displaystyle |}{\underset{\displaystyle H}{C}}-\overset{\displaystyle |}{\underset{\displaystyle OH}{C}}-$$

2. Alcohols   (R - OH)

a. Dehydration of Alcohols to Yield an Olefin

$$-\overset{\displaystyle |}{\underset{\displaystyle H}{C}}-\overset{\displaystyle |}{\underset{\displaystyle OH}{C}}- \ \xrightarrow{H^+} \ -C = C- \ + \ H_2O$$

b. Oxidation of Alcohols (where [O] is a general oxidizing agent)

(i) Primary:

$$RCH_2-OH \xrightarrow{[O]} \underset{\text{aldehyde}}{R-\overset{\displaystyle O}{\overset{\|}{C}}-H} \xrightarrow{[O]} \underset{\substack{\text{carboxylic}\\\text{acid}}}{R-\overset{\displaystyle O}{\overset{\|}{C}}-OH}$$

(ii) Secondary:

$$R-\underset{\displaystyle OH}{\overset{\displaystyle |}{C}H}-R' \xrightarrow{[O]} \underset{\text{ketone}}{R-\overset{\displaystyle O}{\overset{\|}{C}}-R'}$$

(iii) Tertiary: Tertiary alcohols cannot be oxidized.

3. Thiols   R-SH

  a. Oxidation of Thiols to Form a Disulfide Bond.

$$2 \text{ R-S-H} \xrightarrow{\text{[O]}} \text{R-S-S-R}$$
$$\text{disulfide}$$

  b. Reduction of Disulfides (where [R] is a general reducing agent)

$$\text{R-S-S-R} \xrightarrow{\text{[R]}} 2 \text{ R-S-H}$$

4. Aldehydes

$$\text{R- C - H}$$
$$\|$$
$$\text{O}$$

  a. Oxidation

$$\begin{array}{ccc}
\text{R-C-H} & \xrightarrow{\text{[O]}} & \text{R-C-OH} \\
\| & & \| \\
\text{O} & & \text{O} \\
& & \text{carboxylic acid}
\end{array}$$

  b. Reduction

$$\begin{array}{ccc}
\text{R-C-H} & \xrightarrow{\text{[R]}} & \text{R-CH}_2\text{-OH} \\
\| & & \text{primary alcohol} \\
\text{O} & &
\end{array}$$

  c. Hemiacetal and Acetal Formation
      (reaction of an aldehyde with an alcohol)

$$\begin{array}{ccccccc}
 & & & & \text{OR'} & & \text{OR'} \\
 & & & & | & \xrightleftharpoons[]{\text{H}^+/\text{R'OH}} & | \\
\text{R- C-H} & + & \text{R'-OH} \longrightarrow & \text{R-C-H} & & \text{R-C-H} & + \text{ H}_2\text{O} \\
\| & & & | & & | \\
\text{O} & & & \text{OH} & & \text{OR'} \\
\text{aldehyde} & & \text{alcohol} & \text{hemiacetal} & & \text{acetal}
\end{array}$$

d. Aldol Condensation
     (combination of two carbonyl compounds to form an
     aldol - a ß-hydroxy carbonyl)

$$\underset{\text{ketone}}{R_1 - \overset{\overset{\textstyle O}{\|}}{C} - \overset{\overset{\textstyle R_3}{|}}{\underset{\underset{\textstyle R_2}{|}}{C}} - H} \; + \; \underset{\text{aldehyde}}{\overset{\overset{\textstyle O}{\|}}{C} - R_4} \; \begin{array}{c} \longrightarrow \\ \longleftarrow \end{array} \; \underset{\substack{\text{aldol} \\ \text{(ß-hydroxy carbonyl)}}}{R1 - \overset{\overset{\textstyle O}{\|}}{C} - \overset{\overset{\textstyle R_3}{|}}{\underset{\underset{\textstyle R_2}{|}}{C}} - \overset{\overset{\textstyle O\,H}{|}}{\underset{\underset{\textstyle H}{|}}{C}} - R4}$$

e. Reversible Isomerization of Ketose and an Aldose

$$\underset{\text{Ketose}}{\overset{\textstyle CH_2OH}{\underset{\textstyle R}{\overset{|}{\underset{|}{C=O}}}}} \qquad \begin{array}{c} \dashrightarrow \\ \longleftarrow \end{array} \qquad \underset{\text{Aldose}}{\overset{\overset{\textstyle O}{\|}}{C} - H \atop \underset{\textstyle R}{\overset{|}{H - C - OH}}}$$

5. **Ketones** $R - \overset{\|}{\underset{O}{C}} - R'$

a. Oxidation - no reaction

b. Reduction

$$R - \overset{\|}{\underset{O}{C}} - R' \quad \xrightarrow{[R]} \quad \underset{\text{secondary alcohol}}{R - \overset{\overset{\textstyle H}{|}}{\underset{\underset{\textstyle OH}{|}}{C}} - R'}$$

26

c. Keto-enol Tautomerism (for guanine)

Keto tautomer   Enol tautomer

d. Hemiketal and Ketal Formation

$$\begin{array}{ccc} & OR'' & OR'' \\ & | & H^+/R''OH \quad | \\ R\text{-}C\text{-}R' + R''\text{-}OH \longrightarrow & R\text{-}C\text{-}R' \xrightarrow[\longleftarrow]{} & R\text{-}C\text{-}R' + H_2O \\ \| & | & | \\ O & OH & OR'' \\ ketone \quad\quad alcohol & hemiketal & ketal \end{array}$$

e. Aldol Condensation (see above)

6. __Carboxylic Acids__   R - C - OH
                                  ‖
                                  O

a. Reduction

$$\begin{array}{ccc} & [R] & [R] \\ R\text{-}C\text{-}OH \xrightarrow{\quad\quad} & R\text{-}C\text{-}H \xrightarrow{\quad\quad} & R\text{-}CH_2\text{-}OH \\ \| & \| & \\ O & O & \\ & aldehyde & primary\ alcohol \end{array}$$

b. Decarboxylation

Carboxylic acids with a α-carbonyl group undergo loss of CO_2 (decarboxylation) when heated.

$$
\begin{array}{ccc}
\text{O} & \text{O} & & \text{O} \\
\| & \| & \text{Heat} & \| \\
\text{HO - C - C - OH} & & \text{--------->} & \text{HO - C - H} + CO_2
\end{array}
$$

7. <u>Esters</u>

$$
\begin{array}{c}
\text{R - C - OR'} \\
\| \\
\text{O}
\end{array}
$$

a. Preparation of Esters

$$
\begin{array}{cccc}
\text{O} & & & \text{O} \\
\| & & & \| \\
\text{R - C - OH} & + & \text{R' - OH} \quad \text{------->} & \text{R - C - O - R'} + H_2O
\end{array}
$$

b. Hydrolysis (in basic or acidic aqueous solution)

$$
\begin{array}{ccc}
& \text{OH}^- & \\
\text{R - C - O - R'} & \text{--------->} & \text{R - C - O}^- + \text{R' - OH} \\
\| & & \| \\
\text{O} & & \text{O}
\end{array}
$$

$$
\begin{array}{ccc}
& \text{H}^+ & \\
\text{R - C - O - R'} & \text{--------->} & \text{R - C - OH} + \text{R' - OH} \\
\| & & \| \\
\text{O} & & \text{O}
\end{array}
$$

28

c. Claisen Condensation

(This ester condensation reaction is similar to the aldol condensation, but here the -OR group of the ester is the leaving group. Therefore, the **Claisen condensation is a substitution reaction**, while the **aldol condensation is an addition reaction**).

$$\underset{\text{}}{RCH_2\overset{\displaystyle O}{\overset{\|}{C}}-OR'} \; + \; \underset{\displaystyle R}{\underset{|}{H-CH}\overset{\displaystyle O}{\overset{\|}{C}OR'}} \quad \xrightarrow{\text{base}} \quad RCH_2\overset{\displaystyle O}{\overset{\|}{C}}-\underset{\displaystyle R}{\underset{|}{CH}}\overset{\displaystyle O}{\overset{\|}{C}OR'} \; + \; R'OH$$

a β-keto ester

8. <u>Amines</u> $\qquad NH_nR_{(3-n)}$

Schiff Base Formation

$$\underset{\substack{\text{carbonyl} \\ \text{compound}}}{R-\overset{\displaystyle O}{\overset{\|}{C}}-H} \; + \; \underset{\substack{\text{substituted} \\ \text{amine}}}{R'-NH_2} \quad \xrightarrow{H^+} \quad \underset{\substack{\text{Schiff base} \\ \text{(substituted imine)}}}{R-\overset{\displaystyle H}{\overset{|}{C}}=NR'}$$

9. <u>Amides</u> $\qquad \underset{\displaystyle NH_nR_{(3-n)}}{\underset{|}{R-C=O}}$

a. Peptide Bond (Amide) Formation

see next page

$$\underset{\substack{R \; O}}{\underset{|\;\;\|}{H_2N-C-C-O-H}} \; + \; \underset{\substack{R \; O}}{\underset{|\;\;\|}{H-N-C-C-OH}} \xrightarrow{\text{DCC}} \underset{\substack{R \; O \quad R}}{\underset{|\;\;\|\;\;\;\;|}{H_2NC-C-N-CCO_2H}} \; + \; H_2O$$

29

(DDC = dicyclohexylcarbodiimide, which activates the carboxyl group.

b. Hydrolysis

$$R - \overset{\overset{\textstyle O}{\|}}{C} - NR_2 \quad \xrightarrow{\text{H}^+} \quad R - \overset{\overset{\textstyle O}{\|}}{C} - OH \quad + \quad NH_2R_2^+$$

$$R - \overset{\overset{\textstyle O}{\|}}{C} - NR_2 \quad \xrightarrow{\text{OH}^-} \quad R - \overset{\overset{\textstyle O}{\|}}{C} - O^- \quad + \quad NHR_2$$

10. **Esters of Phosphoric Acid**

$$HO - \overset{\overset{\textstyle O}{\|}}{\underset{\underset{\textstyle OH}{|}}{P}} - O - R$$

Hydrolysis

$$HO - \overset{\overset{\textstyle O}{\|}}{\underset{\underset{\textstyle OH}{|}}{P}} - O - R \quad \xrightarrow{\text{H}_2\text{O}} \quad HO - \overset{\overset{\textstyle O}{\|}}{\underset{\underset{\textstyle OH}{|}}{P}} - OH \quad + \quad R\text{-}OH$$

EXERCISES

1.   Name all the classes of organic compounds that contain the following:

       a. a carbonyl group.

       b. a nitrogen atom.

       c. a hydroxyl group.

2.   Write out the equation for the reaction of the following molecules and show the structures for the reactants and products:

       a. butyric acid and propanol.

       b. phosphoric acid and ethanol.

       c. phosphoric acid and 5'-adenosine diphosphate (5'-ADP) to produce 5'-adenosine triphosphate (5'-ATP) containing an additional acid anhydride bond. Hint: The reaction occurs at the point shown in the figure of 5'-ADP.

Reaction site

Adenosine diphosphate (ADP)

d. Glycerol and an of excess of the saturated fatty acid, $H_3C(CH_2)_{14}COOH$.

3.   a.   The structure for the α–amino acid, lysine, is shown to the right. Indicate the Greek letter which designates the starred (*) carbon connected to the amine group in the side chain?

$$NH_3^+$$
$$|$$
$$HOOCCH$$
$$|~~~~~~~~~~~*$$
$$CH_2CH_2CH_2CH_2NH_3^+$$

b.   Draw the structure for the substituted lysine, 5-hydroxylysine.

4. Identify the functional groups in the compounds shown below.

a.

Adenosine

b. acetylcholine

$$\underset{\substack{O \\ \parallel}}{H_3C-C-OCH_2CH_2\overset{+}{N}(CH_3)_3}$$

c. Arachidonic acid

$$CH_3(CH_2)_4CH=CHCH_2CH=CHCH_2CH=CHCH_2CH=CH(CH_2)_3COOH$$

d.

Folic Acid

Pteridine derivative   p-Aminobenzoic acid   Glutamic acid

33

e.   Nicotinamide adenine dinucleotide (NAD⁺, NADH)

Reduced form   Oxidized form

5.   D-ribose and D-fructose are both monosaccharides. The D-ribose is described as an <u>aldopentose</u>, while the D-fructose is a <u>ketohexose</u>. Refer to Figure 4.3 in the text and note the open chain configurations. Point out how the underlined names help describe these molecules.

ANSWERS TO EXERCISES

1.   a.   a carbonyl group: aldehydes, ketones, carboxylic acids, esters (including lactones which are cyclic esters) and amides.
        b.   a nitrogen atom: amines and amide.
        c.   an -OH group: alcohols and carboxylic acids.

2.   a.

$$H_3CCH_2CH_2COOH + H_3CCH_2CH_2OH \longrightarrow H_3CCH_2CH_2\overset{\displaystyle O}{\overset{\|}{C}} - O - CH_2CH_2CH_3$$

$$+ H_2O$$

      b.

$$HO - \overset{\displaystyle O}{\underset{\displaystyle OH}{\overset{\|}{P}}} - OH \quad + \quad H_3CH_2OH \longrightarrow \quad {}^- O - \overset{\displaystyle O}{\underset{\displaystyle O^-}{\overset{\|}{P}}} - O - CH_2CH_3$$

$$+ \ H_2O + 2H^+$$

      c.

ADP (structure shown in question)   + H_3PO_4 ------->

Adenosine triphosphate (ATP)

35

For convenience, the phosphoric acid reactant in both reactions 2b and 2c, is written as the completely protonated form and the dissociated form in the formation of the ester and the anhydride products.

d.

$$
\begin{array}{l}
CH_2-OH \\
| \\
CH-OH \quad + \quad excess \quad R-\overset{\overset{O}{\|}}{C}-OH \quad \longrightarrow \\
| \\
CH_2-OH
\end{array}
\qquad
\begin{array}{l}
CH_2-O-\overset{\overset{O}{\|}}{C}-R \\
| \\
CH-O-\overset{\overset{O}{\|}}{C}-R \quad + \quad 3\ H_2O \\
| \\
CH_2-O-\underset{\underset{O}{\|}}{C}-R
\end{array}
$$

3.

a.

$$
\begin{array}{l}
NH_3^+ \\
| \\
HC-COOH \\
| \\
CH_2-CH_2-CH_2-CH_2-NH_3^+ \\
\beta \qquad \delta \qquad \gamma \qquad \varepsilon
\end{array}
$$

The amino group on the side chain is on the epsilon (ε) carbon.

b. In the IUPAC nomenclature, the numbering of the carbon atoms start at the acid group. Therefore, the structure for 5-hydroxylysine is:

$$
\begin{array}{c}
\quad NH_3^+ \qquad\qquad OH \\
\quad | \qquad\qquad\quad | \\
HOOC-CH-CH_2-CH_2-CH-CH_2-NH_3^+
\end{array}
$$

Position--->   1   2   3   4   5   6

4.   a.   alkene, amines, alcohols, ether
       b.   ester, quaternary amine
       c.   alkene, carboxylic acid
       d.   amines, alcohol, amide, carboxylic acids, (aromatic character)
       e.   amines, alcohol, ether, alkenes, phosphate esters, acid (phosphate) anhydride

5.   The underlined descriptions indicate three points: (1) the molecule is a sugar (the suffix -ose), (2) it contains a ketone or an aldehyde (the prefix keto- or aldo-), and (3) it contains 5(pent-) or 6 (hex-) carbons. Note that in a sugar with n carbon atoms, there are (n-1) alcohol groups, with one alcohol group on each carbon.

5

Amino Acids and Peptides

This chapter presents the amino acids, with the emphasis on the elementary acid-base chemistry and the structure of the side chain groups. The only structural difference between each of the 20 amino acids is the side chain group, which determines the distinctive character of the amino acid. Although the side groups are routinely classified according to whether they are 1) nonpolar, 2) neutral polar, 3) acidic or 4) basic, additional characteristics to take note of are the size, shape, charge and the chemical reactivity of the individual groups. The amino acids are amphoteric in character and therefore their form and properties are dependent on the pH of the solution. The zwitterion is the form of the amino acid which has a **net** zero charge. The reaction of two amino acids to produce a dipeptide, linked by a peptide bond, exemplifies the condensation reaction common in the formation of larger peptides and proteins. The peptide bond, along with the carbonyl bond, exhibits partial double bond character and therefore this peptide unit is planar. The single bonds to the α-carbon atom exhibit various degrees of restricted rotation, depending on the character of the side chain group.

CHAPTER OBJECTIVES

1.   Indicate the difference between stereoisomers such as the D- and the L-isomers of an amino acid.

2.   Characterize the amino acids according to whether the side group is aromatic, polar or non-polar, positively or negatively charged, has a chemical functional group and/or can participate in hydrogen bonding interactions.

3.   Calculate the pH at which the zwitterion exists in aqueous solution for a nonpolar, a basic and an acidic amino acid.

4.   Make a plot of a titration curve for a nonpolar, acidic and a basic amino acid and indicate the species that are present after the addition of 0.5, 1.0, 1.5, 2.0 (2.5, 3.0, also for the acidic or basic amino acids) equivalents of base.

5.   Explain the basis of electrophoresis and how this technique can be used to separate a mixture of amino acids.

6.   Draw the structure of a tripeptide, indicating the N-terminal and C-terminal residues, the peptide bonds, and the atoms in the peptide backbone and in the side groups which may participate in a hydrogen bond.

7.   Draw the resonance structures for the peptide bond which are consistent with its planarity.

8.   Draw the structure for glutathione in the oxidized and reduced forms, pointing out the unusual peptide linkage.

9.   List some small cyclic peptides and indicate their physiological functions.

EXERCISES

1.   Specify the amino acid(s) which has a **side chain group** with the following characteristics.

a.   Is positively charged at neutral pH.   _____

b.   Has an alcohol (or phenolic) functional group.

_____

c. Contains a thiol.   _____

d. Has aromatic character.   _____

e. Contains an amide functional group.   _____

f. Can participate in hydrogen bonding.   _____

2. List the **amino acids** which exhibit the following characteristics.

a. Is positively charged at pH 7.   _____

b. Is negatively charged at pH 7.   _____

c. Can form disulfide bonds.   _____

d. Is not chiral.   _____

e. Has more than one chiral carbon.   _____

3. Draw the structure for the zwitterion of alanine and lysine and indicate the pH at which they would exist. The pK values for alanine are 2.34 and 9.69, while those for lysine are 2.18, 8.95 (α-NH$_3$) and 10.53 (side chain).   ala $2.34 + 9.69 = 12.03 \div 2 = 6.01$

⊕-lys-⊖ ⇌ ⊕-lys-⊖ ⇌ 0-lys-⊖ ⇌ 0-lys-⊖

+2 pH2.18   +1 pH8.95   0   pH=10.53

10.53
8.95
2⟌19.48
9.74

4. Three amino acids, gly, ser and trp, react to produce a tripeptide. Indicate all possible products in the reaction. Specify the amino and carboxyl terminal residues in the products.

5. Glutathione is perhaps the most abundant peptide in living systems. However, this tripeptide has a very unusual structure. The descriptive name for glutathione is, γ-glutamyl-L-cysteinylglycine. Draw the tripeptide and indicate how the nomenclature for naming this tripeptide defines its structure.

40

6. Draw the conjugate acid and conjugate base pair for aspartic acid that exists at the following pH values: a) pH = 2.09; b) pH = 3.86; and c) pH = 9.82.

Hint: These pH values correspond to the 3 pK_a values for aspartic acid. There is a different acid and base conjugate pair at each of these points.

7. Consider the titration of histidine. What species exist in solution after the following number of equivalents of NaOH have been added? Briefly justify your answer.

    a.   0.5 equivalents
    b   1.0 equivalent
    c.   2.5 equivalents

8. Consider the following two peptides:

    i. arg-asp-cys-his-lys   and   ii. ala-ile-phe-trp-met

    a.   Which peptide would exhibit the simpler titration curve?
    b.   How many groups can be titrated in each peptide?
    c.   Which peptide can be oxidized to produce a cystine linkage?
    d.   Which peptide would be the more soluble in water?
    e.   The zwitterionic form of which peptide would occur at the lower pH value?

9. Electrophoresis can be used to separate molecules of different charge. An electric field can be set up {(+) ----------(-)} in a stationary matrix material. If the amino acids were placed in the middle of the material, neutral species would not migrate from this position. However, the positively charged species would migrate toward the negative electrode, while the negatively charged species would travel in the opposite direction toward the positive electrode. If a drop of solution at pH 5, containing asp, his, ala and lys, were placed in the middle of the material, indicate how the electric field would effect the position of each of the amino acids.

10. The structure for morphine is shown below, together with the formula for the pentapeptide, methionine enkephalin.

Morphine has a potent physiological activity which mimics that of the enkephalin. Can you suggest a possible reason for this property?

what is that physiological activity?

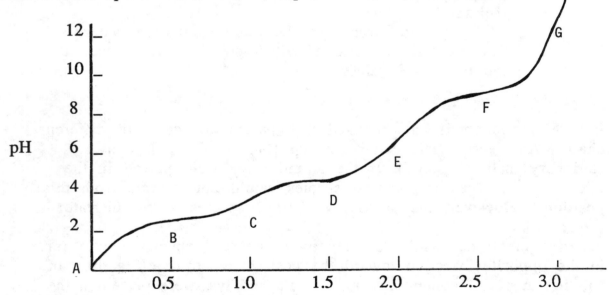

Morphine

Methionine enkephalin is: tyr-gly-gly-phe-met

11. The idealized titration curve for glutamic acid is drawn below. What are the species which exist at points A-G on the diagram?

pH

12
10
8
6
4
2

A B C D E F G

0.5   1.0   1.5   2.0   2.5   3.0

Moles of NaOH added per mole of glutamic acid

42

ANSWERS TO EXERCISES

1. a. lys, arg, his (ca. 10%)
   b. ser, thr, (tyr)
   c. cys
   d. phe, tyr, trp
   e. gln, asn
   f. arg, lys, his, glu, asp, asn, gln, ser, thr, tyr, trp

2. a. arg, lys, his (ca. 10%)
   b. asp, glu
   c. cys
   d. gly
   e. thr, ile

3.

$$
\begin{array}{ccc}
CH_3 & & CH_2CH_2CH_2CH_2NH_3^+ \\
| & & | \\
H\text{-}C\text{-}COO^- & & H\text{-}C\text{-}COO^- \\
| & & | \\
NH_3^+ & & NH_2
\end{array}
$$

alanine, pH = 6.01   lysine, pH = 9.74

The pH at which the zwitterion exists is called the isoelectric point (pI) for the amino acid. This pH value is calculated by determining the **average value of the two pK$_a$ values which "strattle" the pH domain in which the zwitterionic form resides**.

For amino acids with side groups which are not acidic or basic, such as alanine, the pI value is simply the average of pK$_{a1}$ and pK$_{a2}$.

$$
\begin{aligned}
pI &= 1/2 \, [pK_{a1} + pK_{a2}] \\
&= 1/2 \, [2.34 + 9.69] = \underline{6.01}
\end{aligned}
$$

43

For amino acids which have either an acidic or basic side chain, the pI value is again the average of two appropriate pK values, one of which is always the pK_R, the pK for the side group. For lysine, a basic amino acid, pK_{a2}, is the other pK value which strattles the pH domain of the zwitterion. For acidic amino acids, such as aspartic acid and glutamic acid, pK_{a1}, is used.

$$pI = 1/2 \ [pK_R + pK_{a2}]$$
$$= \ 1/2 \ [8.95 + 10.53] = \underline{9.74}$$

4.   The tripeptide products of this reaction will include all sequence combinations of the three amino acid residues. Therefore, there will be 9 different products. These are listed below, with the amino terminal residue written to the left and the carboxyl terminal residue on the right.

gly-gly-gly	ser-ser-ser	trp-trp-trp
gly-trp-ser	ser-gly-trp	trp-ser-gly
gly-ser-trp	ser-trp-gly	trp-gly-ser

$$+$$
$$H_3N\text{----------------}CO_2{}^-$$
(N-terminal residue)   (C-terminal residue)

5.   γ-glu-cys-gly

```
        H              O   H O H  H
      + |              ||  | || |  |
  H3N- C- CH2-CH2- C- N- C- C- N- C- COO -
      |              |  |           |
      COO-           H  CH2         H
                        |
                        S-H
```

There are two peptide bonds in glutathione. The peptide bond between the cysteine and glycine residues is normal. The second peptide bond is unusual in that it is between the γ-carboxyl (the side group) of the glutamic acid residue and the amino end of the cysteine residue.

6.

a. The species at pH = 2.09 are:

Conjugate acid | Conjugate base

b. The species at pH = 3.86 are:

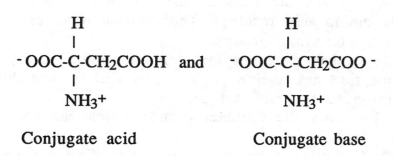

Conjugate acid | Conjugate base

c. The species at pH = 9.82 are:

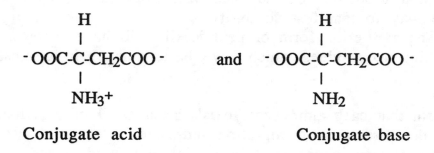

Conjugate acid | Conjugate base

7. a. After the addition of one-half equivalent of base, one-half of the carboxylic acid will be neutralized. This is the point at which equal amounts of the acid and the conjugate base are present {his(COOH) = his(COO⁻)}.

   After the addition of one equivalent of base, all of the protons from the acid group (-COOH) have been titrated.

   After two and one-half equivalents have been added, all the protons in the acid group (one equivalent) and the protons in the side chain (hisH⁺) group (the second equivalent) have been neutralized. In addition, half of the protons from the amino group (-NH₃⁺) have been neutralized.

8. a. Peptide (ii) has the simpler titration curve since there are no acidic or basic amino acid residues. The titration involves only the amino- and carboxyl-terminal groups.

   b. Peptide (i) has 7 groups that can be titrated. Every amino acid in the pentapeptide has a side chain group with a titratable hydrogen, in addition to the terminal groups.

   Peptide (ii) has only the terminal groups which can be titrated by base.

   c. Peptide (i) only. It has a cysteine in it. Two molecules of this peptide can form a cystine bond.

   d. Peptide (i) will be more soluble. Even though both peptides are about the same molecular weight, peptide (i) has many charged groups to interact with water. Peptide (ii) contains only hydrophobic and aromatic residues and will not interact with water in a positive way to manifest solubility.

   e. The zwitterion form of peptide (ii) will have a lower pH since it contains no residues which have basic side chain groups.

9. The form that each amino acid exists as at a pH of 5 is listed below, with the direction of migration indicated.

asp;	negatively charged;	will migrate toward + end
his;	positively charged;	will migrate toward - end
ala;	neutral;	will not migrate
lys;	positively charged;	will migrate toward - end

10.

Morphine

tyr-gly-gly-phe-met

Note that tyrosine, being the amino terminal residue of the met enkephalin, is structurally very similar to that in the upper, left-hand part of the morphine structure. Therefore, it is thought that both molecules may interact in a similar way with the same cellular target.

11.   Point A;   100% completely protonated form;
                  species with a (+1) charge
      Point B;   50% of the species with (+1) charge and
                  50% zwitterion
      Point C;   100% zwitterion species
      Point D;   50% zwitterion species and 50% of the species
                  with (-1) charge
      Point E: 100% of the species with (-1) charge
      Point F;   50% of the species with (-1) charge and 50% of
                  species with (-2) charge
      Point G;   100% of the species with (-2) charge

6

Carbohydrates

Carbohydrates are polyhydroxy aldehydes or polyhydroxy ketones. Their primary function is to serve as an energy source in plants and animals, in addition to acting as essential structural elements in plants. The chemical reactivity is associated with the main functionalities-those of the alcohol, aldehyde and/or ketone, hemiacetal and hemiketal-found in the carbohydrates. The molecules are portrayed in the Fisher projection formulas, or alternatively, in the Haworth projection formulas for the cyclic structures. Chiral centers abound in the aldoses and ketoses, with stereoisomers in the form of enantiomers, diastereomers, epimers and anomers. Linkage of two or more monosaccharides to form di-, oligo- or polysaccharides (glycosides) involves the formation of one or more glycosidic bonds, with the conversion of a terminal hemiacetal to an acetal linkage. These glycosidic backbones may be either α- or β-linkages, with the connectivity most often being between the C1-carbon on one monosaccharide and the C4-carbon of the other. Additional diversity in the structure and the function of these molecules is derived through (1) chemical modification of the monosaccharides, (2) many different monosaccharides in the make-up of a polysaccharide, together with (3) additional or different types of glycosidic linkages between the monomeric units.

CHAPTER OBJECTIVES

1. Be able to recognize stereoisomers and distinguish between enantiomers and diastereomers, including epimers and anomers.
2. Draw the Fisher projection formulas for aldoses and ketoses and classify the molecules according to the type of stereoisomer.
3. Convert Fisher projection formulas for aldohexoses into the corresponding Haworth formulas.
4. Point out in both the Fisher and Haworth formulas the carbon atom which defines the D- or the L-family of stereoisomers.
5. Indicate the chemical basis for a mono- or disaccharide being a reducing or nonreducing sugar.
6. Write the equations for monosaccharides undergoing (1) reduction, (2) esterification and (3) glycoside formation.
7. Draw the structures for the reactants and products in the formation of sucrose, lactose and maltose. Point out the anomeric carbon atoms and the type of linkages formed in the products.
8. Catalog the similarities and differences in the structure and function of the major polysaccharides.
9. Characterize a typical glycoprotein and indicate some functions for them.

EXERCISES

1. Classify each of the following monosaccharides (e. g., as an aldotetrose) and indicate the number of chiral carbon atoms in each molecule.

a.

CHO
|
HO-C-H
|
H-C-OH
|
HO-C-H
|
CH₂OH

b. CHO
|
H-C-OH
|
HO-C-H
|
HO-C-H
|
HO-C-H
|
CH₂OH

c.

CH₂OH
|
C= O
|
CH₂OH

d.

$$
\begin{array}{c}
CHO \\
| \\
H\text{-}C\text{-}OH \\
| \\
CH_2OH
\end{array}
$$

e.

$$
\begin{array}{c}
H \\
| \\
C=O \\
| \\
H\text{---}C\text{---}OH \\
| \\
HO\text{---}C\text{---}H \\
| \\
H\text{---}C\text{---}OH \\
| \\
H\text{---}C\text{---}OH \\
| \\
CH_2OH
\end{array}
$$

D-Glucose

2.   Indicate whether the monosaccharides in question 1 are in the D- or L-form, if either.

3.   Indicate which of the following molecules can be classified as monosaccharides, disaccharides, aldehydes, ketones, hemiacetal, acetal, hemiketals or ketals. Some of the molecules can be classified in more than one category.

a.

CH₃
|
C = O
|
CH₂
|
CH₃

b.

c.

CHO

d.

OCH₂CH₃
|
H₃C-C-H
|
OH

e.

CHO
|
HO-C-H
|
CH₂OH

f.

CH₂OH
|
C = O
|
HO-C-H
|
H-C-OH
|
H-C-OH
|
CH₂OH

g.   Sucrose

h.   Lactose

51

4. Define diastereomer and epimer. Give an example of two diastereomers which are epimers and two diastereomers which are not epimers.

5. a. Draw the structure of α–D-glucose in the Haworth projection formula (ring) and point out the anomeric carbon.
   b. Indicate the atoms in the corresponding Fisher projection formula which will react with each other to form the cyclic hemiacetal structure.

6. The Fisher projections for D-ribose and L-gulose are shown below.

D-ribose   L-gulose

a. Draw the Fisher projections for L-ribose and D-gulose.
b. Draw Haworth projections for D- and L-ribose in the α–form and for the D- and L-gulose in the β-form.
c. How many enantiomers are there for L-gulose?

7. Which of the molecules shown in problem 3 will give a positive Tollen's test?

8.   As discussed in the answer for question 7, a ketose gives a positive Tollen's test because it can be converted to an aldose through an enediol intermediate. Draw the structures for a ketose, an aldose and the enediol and indicate which of these molecules are enantiomers or diastereomers.

9.   Cellulose, the most abundant organic compound in the biosphere, is a linear, homopolysaccharide of D-glucose. Humans, however, can not digest it. Briefly explain this.

10.   a.   Give two examples of a mucopolysaccharide.
      b.   What are the common characteristics of mucopolysaccharides?

11.   Amylose is digested by a pair of enzymes.
      a.   Name the hydrolytic enzymes and indicate the specific nature of the cleavage reaction and the products formed.
      b.   Amylopectin requires (the action of) three enzymes for complete digestion. In addition to the two enzymes used to digest amylose, what is the additional enzyme and what is its role?

12.   Human blood groups are classified as A, B, AB or O type.
      a.   How are oligosaccharides important in this classification? Where are these glycoproteins found in blood cells?
      b.   What monosaccharides are important in distinguishing the different blood types?

13.   Match the polysaccharide in the left column with the correct description on the right.

a. cellulose   _____   1.   polymer of primarily D-
                                         galacturonic acid

b. chitin   _____   2.   polysaccharide used as an
                                         anticoagulant

c. heparin   _____   3.   linear homopolysaccharide of
                                         D-glucose

d. pectin   _____   4.   main storage polymer for
                                         carbohydrates in animals

e. glycogen   _____   5.   found in the exoskeleton of
                                         insects

53

ANSWERS TO EXERCISES

1. a. aldopentose, 3
    b. aldoheptose, 5
    c. ketotriose, 0
    d. aldotriose, 1
    e. aldohexose, 4

2. In the Fisher formula, a monosaccharide is a member of the **D-family** if the -OH group on the chiral carbon farthest from the C1 carbon is on the **RIGHT** side. For the *L-family*, the corresponding -OH group is on the *LEFT*.

In the Haworth formula, the terminal -CH_2OH group is positioned **ABOVE** the ring in the **D-family** or alternatively *BELOW* the plane of the ring in the *L-family*.

Therefore, the key relationship between the groups on a Fisher and Haworth formula is:

Groups on the **RIGHT** in the Fisher formula are directed **DOWN** in the Haworth formula.

Groups on the *LEFT* in the Fisher formula are directed *UP* in the Haworth formula.

    a. L-form
    b. L-form
    c. no stereoisomers
    d. D-form
    e. D-form

3. a. ketone
    b. none (this is an ether)
    c. aldehyde
    d. hemiacetal
    e. monosaccharide, aldehyde
    f. monosaccharide, ketone
    g. disaccharide, acetal
    h. disaccharide, acetal, hemiacetal

4.   Diastereomers are any two stereoisomers which are not enantiomers. Epimers are diastereomers which differ in the configuration at only one of the chiral carbon atoms.

Diastereomers which are epimers.	Diastereomers which are not epimers.

5.   The Haworth projection formula for α–D-glucose is:

Anomeric carbon

The Fisher projection for α-D-glucose is:

```
          CHO ←
           |
        H-C-OH
           |
       HO-C-H
           |
        H-C-OH
           |
        H-C-OH ←
           |
         CH₂OH
```

6.   a.

L-ribose

D-gulose

b.

L-α-ribose

D-α-ribose

L-β-gulose

D-β-gulose

Enantiomers are PAIRS of stereoisomers which are nonsuperimposable mirror images. Therefore, there is only one enantiomer of L-gulose. It is D-gulose, which is shown above.

7.   A positive Tollen's test indicates that the molecule contains an aldehyde which is readily oxidized to the corresponding acid.
   a.   a ketone; it will not be oxidized.
   b.   an ether; it will not be oxidized.
   c.   an aldehyde; it will be oxidized.
   d.   a non-cyclic hemiacetal; it will not be oxidized.
   e.   an aldehyde; it will be oxidized.
   f.   a ketohexose. This is an exception to the simple rule that ketones can not be oxidized. Ketones which have an -OH group on the adjacent carbon atom (i.e., an α−hydroxy ketone) are oxidized. Therefore, this monosaccharide, like all monosaccharides, whether an aldose or ketose, can be oxidized.
   g.   contains only acetal functionalities which are not oxidized. This is an example of a non-reducing sugar.
   h.   contains a terminal cyclic hemiacetal, which permits ring opening to yield an aldehyde. This is oxidized and is an example of a reducing disaccharide.

8.

```
CH₂OH              CHOH              CHO
 |                  ||                |
C=O      =        C- OH    =     H- C-OH
 |                  |                 |
 R                  R                 R

ketose            enediol          aldose
```

Note that there is both a rearrangement of electrons and hydrogens.

These are diastereomers of D-fructose since they are optical isomers which are not enantiomers (i.e., nonsuperimposable mirror images).

9.   Humans do not have the enzyme, cellulase, which can digest $\beta(1\text{-->}4)$ glycosidic linkages.

10.   a.   Indicate any two of the three mucopolysaccharides mentioned in the chapter:

        Hyaluronic acid
        Chondroitin sulfate
        Heparin

    b.   Common characteristics of mucopolysaccharides are:

        Heteropolysaccharides.
        Highly ionized (negatively charged ionic groups) at
            neutral pH.
        Highly hydrated and involved in hydrogen bonding,
            which yields a gelatinous texture.
        They are found in connective tissue where they serve as
            either a lubricant or cement.

11.   Amylose is a linear polymer of glucose, having α(1-->4) glycosidic connecting bonds. The two enzymes involved in the digestion are:
    a. β-Amylase, an **exo**glycosidase, cleaves from the **non-reducing end** to produce **maltose.**
        α-Amylase, an **endo**glycosidase, hydrolyzes the glycosidic bond **within** the chain to produce **glucose and maltose.**
    b.   Amylopectin is a branched polymer of glucose and therefore also has an α(1-->6) glycosidic bond at the branch points. The additional enzyme needed is the debranching enzyme, which hydrolyzes the α(1-->6) glycosidic linkages.

12.   a.   Glycoproteins are proteins which contain amino acid residues modified with carbohydrate residues. These glycoproteins reside on the surface of erythrocytes in the blood and determine the human blood group.
    b.   L-fucose (Figure 6.10, in the text) is a component of the oligosaccharide in all the blood groups. As shown in Figure 6.29, N-acetylgalactosamine is found at the non-reducing end of the oligosaccharide in type A blood, while in type B, the N-acetylgalactosamine is replaced by α-D-galactose. In type AB blood, both oligosaccharide forms exist, while in type O blood, neither form is found.

13.   a.   3
        b.   5
        c.   2
        d.   1
        e.   4

7

Lipids

Lipids are a diverse family of biomolecules, collectively classified as such because of their solubility in non-polar solvents. Some of the major lipid molecules are fatty acids and the carboxylic- and phosphatidyl-esters of glycerol and sphingosine. The variety and complexity of the lipids can be increased by reaction of a phosphatidic acid with the alcohols, ethanolamine, choline, serine or inositol. These resultant amphiphilic molecules are the major constituents of biological membranes. The ester linkages can be hydrolyzed chemically or alternatively by cellular enzymes called lipases. Steroids represent another major class of lipids, which includes cholesterol, male and female sex hormones, vitamins and bile salts. The fat soluble vitamins, including vitamins, A, D, E, and K serve in a variety of essential biological functions. Two groups of powerful physiological agents, prostaglandins and leukotrienes, both containing 20 carbon atoms, are derived from arachidonic acid and are also members of the lipid family of molecules.

CHAPTER OBJECTIVES

1.   State the criterion for a molecule to be classified as a lipid.
2.   Write the general equation for the reaction of:
     a.   a carboxylic acid and glycerol to form an ester.
     b.   sphingosine and phosphoric acid.
     c.   phosphoric acid and an alcohol.
3.   Distinguish between a triglyceride, phosphatidic acid, a phosphoacylglyceride and a glycolipid.
4.   Point out the common linkages that is found in molecules such as phosphatidylethanolamine, phosphatidylcholine and phosphatidylinositol.
5.   Draw the structure for the general steroid skeleton and name three important molecules which are derived from this basic structure.
6.   Examine the structures of the fat soluble vitamins, point out any functional groups and give two functions for these essential molecules.
7.   Compare the structure of a prostaglandin and a leukotriene molecule with their precursor molecule, arachidonic acid.

SPOTLIGHT

Controversial Drugs: Synthetic Steroids

It is now common knowledge that many professional, and even amateur athletes, take androgenic-anabolic steroids to increase muscle mass and strength. These steroids are synthetic male hormones which were originally synthesized to promote the tissue-building (anabolic) effects and eliminate or reduce their androgenic (masculizing) effects.

In the 1988 Summer Olympic games that were held in Seoul, Korea, a Canadian sprinter, Ben Johnson, ran the 100-meter race in 9.79 seconds to win the gold medal. Drug tests on a urine sample from Johnson revealed that he had significant levels of the anabolic steroid, stanozolol, in his urine. Since the use of anabolic steroids is illegal by Olympic rules, Johnson was stripped of his victory and the Olympic gold medal.

The structures for the female and male sex hormones, estradiol and testosterone, respectively, are shown below and are compared to the synthetic anabolic steroid, stanozolol. Note that common characteristics of male hormones include a methyl group at the carbon atom which serves as the "top" junction for the two six-membered rings in the left of the drawing, in addition to the absence of an aromatic ring in the steroid structure. A five-membered heterocyclic ring has also been added on to make the stanozolol molecule. Stanozolol is but one of the many synthetic anabolic steroids being used by athletes today, despite the many detrimental side-effects which have been reported.

Another controversial synthetic steroid, referred to as RU-486, is a drug developed in France in 1980 to terminate pregnancy. The structure of RU-486 (shown below) is similar to progesterone and it was found to bind to progesterone receptors on the surface of the cell. To the surprise of the biomedical researchers, the binding of RU-486 to the receptors did not produce the same hormonal response within the cell as that produced by progesterone (molecules that exhibit this type of behavior are generally called agonists). Instead the binding blocked any response (molecules of this type are referred to as antagonists). Therefore, RU-486 was a progesterone antagonist and could not only block progesterone binding, but could block its physiological activity. This was the key finding, especially when linked to well established findings that the effects that progesterone produced by its receptor binding were essential for the progression of a successful pregnancy. This has now led to RU-486 being approved for use in abortions in France. Although many successes have been reported, the details of the mechanism of action of this drug and its possible short-term and long-term side effects remain to be elucidated.

Estradiol

Testosterone

Stanozolol

RU-486

EXERCISES

1. a. What is the definition of a lipid?
   b. How does the manner in which one defines a lipid differ from that for carbohydrates, proteins and the other important biomolecules?

2. a. List a number of outstanding general characteristics of fatty acids found in organisms.
   b. Are the double bonds in the unsaturated fatty acids conjugated or isolated?
   c. At which end of the fatty acid does the numbering of the carbons begin?
   d. In four of the five examples of unsaturated fatty acids in Table 7.2, the double bond nearest the acid group is formed between which two carbon atoms? What are the names of these acids? Which acid in the Table is an exception to this observation?

3. Two molecules serve as the backbone for many lipids, including phosphoglycerides and ceramides.
   a. What are the two molecules which serve as the backbone?
   b. Do either of these molecules have any chiral centers?

4. a. What is a lipase and what is its role in biological systems?
   b. What is a chemical method to accomplish this same reaction?

5. Phosphatidylethanolamine (cephalin) and sphingomyelin are both components of membranes. They both have a polar end, with long non-polar segments. Suggest a way in which both of these molecules could be oriented so that a micelle or a lipid bilayer could be formed.

6. Examine the structure of cholesterol in Figure 7.7 in the text.
   a. What functional groups are in cholesterol?
   b. Where is the polar end of this molecule?
   c. Is cholesterol a planar molecule?

7. The melting points for two 16 carbon fatty acids is given below. Palmitic acid is completely saturated, while there is one double bond in palmitoleic acid. Explain the molecular basis for the trend in melting points.

Fatty Acid		**M. P.(^{0}C)**
Palmitic acid	$CH_3(CH_2)_{14}COOH$	63.1
Palmitoleic acid	$CH_3(CH_2)_5CH=CH(CH_2)_7COOH$	- 0.5

8. A five carbon unit called isoprene is found as a reoccurring or often repeating unit in a number of lipids, including some vitamins and/or their precursors. The structure of the unit is:

$$CH_2 = \underset{\underset{CH_3}{|}}{C} - \overset{\overset{H}{|}}{C} = CH_2$$

Examine the structures of β−carotene, vitamin A, D and K, arachidonic acid, prostaglandins and leukotrienes. Does the isoprene unit occur in these molecules?

9. Match the fat soluble vitamin in the left-hand column with its characteristic in the right column.

Vitamin D   a. _____   retinol; involved in vision

Vitamin E   b. _____   regulation of calcium and phosphorus metabolism

Vitamin K   c. _____   contains a bicyclic ring with two carbonyls (a quinone); involved in blood coagulation

Vitamin A   d. _____   antioxidant; reacts with free radicals; active form is α-tocopherol

65

ANSWERS TO EXERCISES

1. a. Lipids are a family of biomolecules which are soluble in non-polar organic solvents, such as ether or chloroform.

   b. Lipids are defined operationally and not by their composition or their function. Therefore, lipid molecules exhibit a wide variety of functions, which include the phospholipids and glycolipids which constitute the lipid bilayer and other components of membranes, steroid hormones, energy stores (e.g., fats) and fat soluble vitamins.

2. a. Fatty acids presented in the chapter have the following characteristics:
   They can be saturated or unsaturated.
   They contain an even number of carbon atoms.
   There are no branched fatty acids.*
   They are amphiphilic in character.
   For unsaturated fatty acids:
      The stereochemistry is cis in virtually all cases.
      The double bonds are isolated and not in a conjugated system.*

   * There are a few rare exceptions to this.

   b. For double bonds to be conjugated, the double bonds must be on adjacent carbons. If the double bonds are on non-adjacent carbons, as in the fatty acids, they are non-conjugated or isolated double bonds.

   Double Bond Systems
   conjugated $\qquad\qquad\qquad\qquad\qquad\qquad\quad$ * $\quad$ *
   (double bonds on adjacent carbons) $\qquad$ $- CH_2 = CH - CH = CH_2 -$

   non-conjugated $\qquad\qquad\qquad\qquad\qquad\quad$ * $\qquad\qquad$ *
   (double bonds on non-adjacent carbons) $\quad$ $- CH = CH - CH_2 - CH = CH-$

   c. The numbering of the carbon atoms starts at the carboxylic acid carbon.

   d. The double bond closest to the acid functional group is between C_9 and C_{10}.

This occurs commonly and is found in palmitoleic (C_{16}), oleic (C_{18}), linoleic (C_{18}) and linolenic (C_{18}) acids. The latter two fatty acids are polyunsaturated. Arachidonic acid is an exception to this general observation.

3.   The two molecules which serve as the backbone in these lipids are glycerol and sphingosine. Although glycerol has no chiral centers, sphingosine has two chiral carbons. Examine Figure 7.6 (in the text) to locate the chiral carbons.

4.   a.   A lipase is an enzyme which catalyzes the cleavage of ester linkages, such as in triglycerides, to form glycerol and fatty acids.
      b.   Acid or basic (called saponification) hydrolysis is a chemical route to accomplish ester hydrolysis. Saponification is the procedure used to produce soaps (Figure 7.3 in the text).

5.   Answer and Figures on the next page.

$$H_3\overset{+}{N} - CH_2 - CH_2 - O - \overset{\overset{O}{\|}}{\underset{\underset{O}{|}}{P}} - O - CH_2$$

Phosphatidylethanolamine

$$(CH_3)_3\overset{+}{N} - CH_2 - CH_2 - O - \overset{\overset{O}{\|}}{\underset{\underset{O}{|}}{P}} - O - CH_2$$

Sphingomyelin

In both cases, the amphiphilic structures can be generally drawn as shown below.

Polar head

Hydrophobic tail

Hydrophobic
Interior

Hydrophilic, Charged
Exterior

A Micelle

Lipid bilayer

Both the micelle and the lipid bilayer structures can form spontaneously in aqueous solution. The hydrophilic polar heads interact favorably with the aqueous solution, while the hydrophobic tails associate favorably with each other and are not exposed to the aqueous solution.

6.   a.   Cholesterol contains an alcohol functional group and has a single double bond.

    b.   The alcohol group is the only polar group in the molecule.

    c.   Cholesterol is a complex, non-planar molecule shown below in the standard presentation and also in the "boat and chair" form conformations.

Cholesterol

7.   The melting point is a function of the **inter**molecular forces between the molecules. In the case of the fatty acids, this involves hydrophobic interactions between the long organic groups. For palmitic acid, the degree of alignment of the saturated chains in the fatty acid is very high, resulting in a high degree of interaction between the molecules. This results in a relatively high melting point.

    On the other hand, with palmitoleic acid, there are a larger number of possible (unfavorable) orientations that an unsaturated organic chain can take. This results in an overall lower degree of alignment and therefore the number of similar interactions between the molecules is decreased. The following Figure generally shows this.

High degree of alignment in
saturated palmitic acid

Degree of alignment is decreased in
unsaturated palmitoleic acid

8.   The isoprene unit is found in β-carotene, 11-cis-retinal, its derivatives (Figure 7.8) and vitamin K.

Vitamin D and E, arachidonic acid, prostaglandins and leukotrienes (Figures 7.10, 11 and 13 in text) do not contain the isoprene units.

9.   a.   Vitamin A
      b.   Vitamin D
      c.   Vitamin K
      d.   Vitamin E

8

Energy Requirements For Life: Thermodynamics

Every reaction has an intrinsic driving force which determines the extent to which it will proceed to completion. As a reaction proceeds and ultimately attains equilibrium, the entropy (S) of the universe (system plus the surroundings) will be a maximum, while the free energy (G) for the molecules (the system) reaches a minimum. In this respect, ΔS_{univ} (>0) and ΔG_{sys} (<0) are fundamental indicators of the spontaneity of any reaction. The standard free energy, ΔG^0, is the free energy difference between the products and the reactants under standard conditions (i.e, 1 M for all solutes and 1 atmosphere for gases at 25^0C). The equilibrium constant, K_{eq}, and the ΔG^0 are really two different means to express this intrinsic driving force. Since most important biochemical reactions are carried out near neutral pH, a standard free energy, $\Delta G^{0'}$, and the equilibrium constant, K'_{eq}, are defined similarly, except that the standard state concentration for hydrogen ions [H^+] is 1×10^{-7} M. The free energy change of a reaction is also related to the enthalpy change, ΔH, for the reacting system and the entropy change of the universe. It is essential to realize that thermodynamic quantities such as G, H and S are state functions. The important property of any of these functions is that the difference in two states [e. g., $\Delta S = (S_{products} - S_{reactants})$] depends only on the initial and final states and not on the route by which the reaction proceeds.

CHAPTER OBJECTIVES

1. State the thermodynamic criteria for the spontaneity of a reaction.
2. Define the thermodynamic quantities which determine if a reaction is at equilibrium and indicate the values they assume.
3. Distinguish between an exergonic and an endergonic process.
4. Write out the mathematical relationships between $\Delta G'$, $\Delta G^{0'}$ and K'_{eq}.
5. State the meaning of the first and second laws of thermodynamics.
6. Define the relationship between free energy, enthalpy and entropy and define ΔH and ΔS in terms that are readily associated with a chemical reaction.

EXERCISES

1. Indicate which of the following statements are true or false. If the statement is false, correct it.

_T_   a. The first law of thermodynamics states that energy can neither be created nor destroyed.

_T_   b. The second law of thermodynamics states that the entropy of the universe is constantly increasing.

_T_   c. The free energy change for a reaction at equilibrium is zero.

_F_   d. The standard free energy change for a reaction at equilibrium is zero.

_T_   e. The enthalpy change of a chemical reaction is derived primarily from the energies of bonds that are broken and formed in the reaction.

_T_   f. The burning of a piece of paper is an example of a reaction which is spontaneous and the entropy will increase.

_F_   g. A reaction which is spontaneous under one particular condition will be spontaneous under all other conditions.

T h. A calorie is greater than a joule of energy.

T i. Thermodynamics indicates whether or not a reaction will proceed spontaneously.

F j. Thermodynamics can be used to indicate how fast a reaction will take place. *Kinetics*

F k. The mixing of oil and water will produce an increase in entropy.

F l. Hydrophobic interactions are spontaneous because of favorable values for both the enthalpy and entropy change. *favorable* *unfavorable or negligible*

T m. Endergonic reactions have a positive free energy change and are not spontaneous.

T n. Endergonic reactions can occur if free energy is supplied from another source, such as the coupling with another reaction.

2. The K_{eq} for the hydrolysis of adenosine monophosphate (AMP) to adenosine (A) and phosphate (P_i) at 25^0 C is $3.0 \times 10^{+2}$.

    a. What are the values of $\Delta G'$ and $\Delta G^{0'}$ for this reaction at equilibrium?

    b. Compare the $\Delta G^{0'}$ for this reaction with that for the hydrolysis of adenosine triphosphate (ATP) to adenosine diphosphate (ADP) and phosphate. What types of bonds are involved in each of these reactions? What can you conclude from these data?

3. ATP is universally considered a carrier of chemical energy which can be used in metabolic reactions. However, the cell also contains the other nucleoside triphosphates, guanosine triphosphate (GTP), thymidine triphosphate (TTP), cytidine triphosphate (CTP) and uridine triphosphate (UTP).

    a. Can these molecules also serve as carriers of chemical energy in a similar manner?

    b. Suggest a possible reason why they are not used in many cases?

4. Consider the reactions below and the associated free energy values.

		ΔG(kJ/mol)
i.	A + B = C	+ 12
ii.	C + D = E	- 32

    a. Will either of these reactions occur spontaneously?

b.   If reaction (i) were written in the opposite way (C = A + B), *yes*
would the reaction be spontaneous? What would be the value of ΔG? *-12*

c.   Hess's Law states that the energy change in a chemical
reaction is the same whether the reaction takes place in one step or
several steps. This law can be used to theoretically calculate the free
energy change for a reaction that has never been studied. Using Hess's
Law, determine the free energy change for the following reaction.

$$A + B + D = E \qquad \Delta G = +12 + (-32) = -20 \text{ kcal/mol}$$

5.   The listing below contains the ΔG^0 values for reactions at 25^0 C.

$\Delta G = -RT \ln k_{eq}$
$\Delta G = (-8.31 \times 10^{-3} \text{ kJ/mol·K})(298) \ln k_{eq}$
$\Delta G = (-2.48) \ln k_{eq}$ *a only*

ΔG^0 (kJ/mol)	
34.3	$9.7 \times 10^{-7} \approx 10 \times 10^{-7} \approx 10^{-6}$
11.4	1×10^{-2}
0.0	1.0
- 5.7	10
- 11.4	$10 \times 10^1 = 1 \times 10^2$
- 34.3	1×10^6

a.   Calculate the corresponding K_{eq} values from each ΔG^0 value
in the listing.   *only 1 hydrogen bond?*

b.   An interaction between two molecules which involves
hydrogen bonding contributes an energy of interaction (ΔG^0) of about 20
kJ/mol. How much greater would the equilibrium constant for an
interaction be if an additional hydrogen bond were involved in the
interaction?   *unclear*

6.   If glucose is completely oxidized to CO_2 and H_2O in a laboratory
experiment, it liberates 2867 kJ/mol of heat energy ($\Delta G^{0'}$ = -2867 kJ/mol).
a.   Write out the balanced equation for this reaction.
b.   Is this an exergonic or endogonic reaction?
c.   What is the form of the energy that is produced? *heat*
d.   This same process is carried out enzymatically in human
cells. Calculate the $\Delta G^{0'}$ for this cellular reaction? What form or forms
does the liberated energy ($\Delta G^{0'}$) take within the cell? *same — coupled to other reactions to produce ATP & energy (other endergonic rxns)*

$$C_6H_{12}O_6 + 6O_2 \rightleftharpoons 6CO_2 + 6H_2O$$

75

In the process of glycolysis, a series of reactions occurs. One of the reactions involves the splitting of the 6-carbon modified sugar, fructose-1,6-bisphosphate, to produce two 3-carbon molecules, dihydroxyacetone and glyceraldehyde-3-phosphate. The standard free energy for this reaction is +23.9 kJ/mol. However, this reaction occurs spontaneously in vivo. Briefly explain.

ANSWERS TO EXERCISES

1.
    a.   True.
    b.   True.
    c.   True.
    d.   False.   The free energy change (ΔG) is zero.
    e.   True.
    f.   True.
    g.   False.   The ΔG value depends on the experimental conditions.
    h.   True.
    i.   True.
    j.   False.   The value of thermodynamic quantities such as ΔG, ΔH, and ΔS are unrelated to the rate of the reaction.
    k.   False.   This is not a spontaneous process and therefore the ΔS_{univ} value will be negative and the ΔG value will be positive.
    l.   False.   Hydrophobic interactions are driven primarily by the increase in entropy.
    m.   True.
    n.   True.

2.   a.   Use the relationship, $\Delta G' = \Delta G^{0'} + 2.303\ RT \log K_{eq}$

Equilibrium is defined as $\underline{\Delta G' = 0.}$
The equation reduces to :
$$\Delta G^{0'} = -2.303RT \log K_{eq}$$

$$= -2.303(8.31\ \text{J mol}^{-1}\text{K}^{-1})(298^0\text{K})\ \log(300)$$

$$\underline{\Delta G^{0'} = -14.2\ \text{kJ/mol}}$$

b.   The value of $\Delta G^{0\prime}$ for the hydrolysis of ATP is 30.5 kJ/mol. This is greater than twice the value for the hydrolysis of AMP. The difference in energy lies in the type of bond that is hydrolyzed. In the case of ATP, an acid anhydride bond is involved, while in AMP hydrolysis, an ester bond is broken. This is a general result of great significance in biochemistry because as will be seen in subsequent chapters, an anhydride bond is considered a "high energy" bond. The hydrolysis of an anhydride bond is used to generate metabolic energy, while an ester bond is not a "high energy" bond and is not a source of energy to the cell.

Note in the following figures, the type of bond hydrolyzed in ATP and AMP.

Adenosine triphosphate
(ATP)

Phosphoester Bond

(AMP) Adenosine monophosphate

3. a. Any of the nucleoside triphosphates could be used as carriers of energy. In all cases, the hydrolysis of the terminal phosphate (an anhydride bond) would produce the same amount of energy as in the hydrolysis of ATP.

b. ATP is primarily used because it is more abundant in the cell than the other nucleoside triphosphates.

4. a. Reaction (i) is not spontaneous since the free energy is positive. Reaction (ii), on the other hand, will take place spontaneously since the free energy change is negative.

b. ΔG for any reverse reaction has the same ΔG value as that for the forward reaction, but with the opposite sign. The ΔG value for the reverse reaction is -12 kJ/mol. Thus, the reaction would be spontaneous if written in this direction.

c. The free energy for the reaction, A + B + D = E, can be determined in this case by simply summing the ΔG values for reactions (i) and (ii). Therefore, the ΔG for this reaction would be <u>-20 kJ/mol.</u> This is an example of an endergonic reaction **coupled** to an exergonic reaction. As a consequence of the coupling, the overall free energy change for the process is negative and the reaction will occur spontaneously. This type of coupling process, especially when involving the hydrolysis of ATP, is very important in biochemistry. The hydrolysis of ATP is coupled to reactions as diverse as transporting ions across membranes and the process of muscle contraction.

5.   a.

ΔG^0 (kJ/mol)	K_{eq}	
-34.3	$1 \times 10^{+6}$	1×10^6
-11.4	$1 \times 10^{+2}$	
0.0	(0.0) 1.0	
(5.7)	1×10^{-1}	
11.4	1×10^{-2}	
34.3	1×10^{-6}	9.7×10^{-7}

errors.

$$\Delta G^\circ = -RT \ln K_{eq}$$

b.   Insertion of the $\Delta G^{0'}$ value of -20 kJ/mol for the hydrogen bonding interaction energy into the equation, $\Delta G^{0'} = -2.303RT \log K_{eq}$, yields a $\underline{K_{eq}\ value\ of\ about\ 3.1 \times 10^{+3}}$. This K_{eq} value would correspond to **the increase** in the value of K_{eq} for an interaction involving an additional hydrogen bond.

6.   a. $C_6H_{12}O_6 + 6 O_2 \longrightarrow 6 CO_2 + 6 H_2O$

b.   This is an exergonic reaction - a spontaneous reaction with a negative free energy change.

c.   The energy from exergonic reactions can be utilized to produce work. In the laboratory experiment, the liberated energy is in the form of heat. No useful work was accomplished.

d.   Since the same reaction is being considered, whether it occurs in a cell or in the laboratory, an identical amount of energy ($\Delta G^{0'}$) is liberated. This exemplifies a characteristic of a thermodynamic state function. That is, the value of a change in a state function (whether ΔG, ΔH, or ΔS) is independent of the route taken to accomplish the reaction (in this case, chemical versus enzymatic).

However, all the energy liberated in the cellular reaction is not lost as heat. A considerable fraction of the energy can be utilized to assist some endergonic cellular reactions to occur. As will become evident in subsequent chapters, this energy is in the form of ATP.

7.   The standard free energy ($\Delta G^{0'}$) gives the free energy value at standard conditions (concentrations at 1 M for solutes, except for [H^+], which is at 1×10^{-7} M). Such standard conditions are not relevant in the cell. The thermodynamic quantity of actual interest and importance is the change in free energy (ΔG). The concentrations in the cell are such that the free energy is negative and therefore, a spontaneous reaction occurs.

9

The Three-Dimensional Structure of Proteins

Proteins are linear polymers of amino acid residues which participate in a wide variety of functions, including the escorting of small molecules between cells, guarding us from the invasion by foreign organisms and playing an instrumental role in sexual development. The unique and complex structure of each protein is determined by the amino acid sequence of the protein. This intricate three-dimensional structural arrangement in space in governed by weak, non-covalent forces between the amino acid residues. Secondary structures, such as α-helices and β-pleated sheets, are held together by hydrogen bonding interactions. The clustering together of these secondary structural units form a supersecondary structure. The unique tertiary structure of a protein is produced by hydrophobic and electrostatic interactions, in addition to hydrogen bonding. Proteins with more than one subunit exhibit an additional level of structure, a quaternary structure, which results from interactions involving any or all of the non-covalent forces. The native structure of a protein is almost always the biologically active form. However, it can be converted to an inactive, denatured form by chemicals or reagents which can disrupt non-covalent forces. Procedures to determine the primary structure (i. e., the sequence) of a protein use chemical reagents and enzymes which cleave at specific sites within the protein. These smaller polypeptide chains can then be sequenced using the Edman degradation procedure. Myoglobin and hemoglobin are metalloproteins which contain a heme prosthetic group in addition to the protein segment. Myoglobin, an oxygen storage protein, is a prototype protein which simply binds to this small molecule (O_2). On the other hand, the four subunit hemoglobin molecule represents an allosteric O_2 carrier, in which O_2 acts as a homotropic effector producing a cooperative binding profile. The O_2 binding profile is further influenced by binding of heterotropic effectors such as H^+, CO_2 and 2,3- bisphosphoglycerate. The influence that H^+ and CO_2 exert on O_2 binding is referred to as the Bohr effect.

A variety of chromatographic and electrophoretic techniques are routinely utilized to separate and characterize amino acids and proteins. These physical techniques take advantage of either differential solubility, the charge of the molecule or selective affinity for another molecule as a means to separate the proteins.

CHAPTER OBJECTIVES

1.   Draw the structure for a dipeptide and point out the peptide bond, the C-terminal and the N-terminal residues.
2.   Name and describe the four levels of protein structure, indicating the types of forces which can be associated with each level of structure.
3.   List the four fundamental bonding interactions found in all proteins and the energy associated with each.
4.   Describe the difference between a structural domain and a subunit.
5.   Explain specifically how extreme pH, detergents, heat, high salt concentration or the addition of a reagent such as urea acts to denature proteins.
6.   Indicate the chemical reagents and enzymes which are used to produce sequence specific cleavage of proteins and describe their specificity.
7.   Outline the reagents and the strategy used in the Edman procedure to sequence peptides.
8.   List the characteristics of an α-helix and the interactions which stabilize it.

9. Characterize the structure and the bonding in a β-pleated sheet and indicate the difference between a parallel and an anti-parallel β-pleated sheet.

10. Describe the characteristics of a supersecondary structure and what specifically constitutes a β-barrel.

11 Characterize the structure and bonding in a collagen helix and describe how it differs from an α-helix.

12. Describe the structure of myoglobin and explain the role of the prosthetic group in its function.

13. Discuss the O_2 binding curve for myoglobin and hemoglobin and indicate how this reflects the nature of the binding of O_2 in each metalloprotein.

14. Indicate how H^+, CO_2 and 2,3-bisphosphoglycerate influence the binding of O_2 in hemoglobin.

Interchapter A

1. Describe the characteristic features of chromatography and the physical basis for the separation of proteins by HPLC and ion exchange chromatography.

2. Outline the basis for separating amino acids or peptides by paper chromatography and electrophoresis, pointing out the unique features of SDS-PAGE.

3. Describe the unique features involved in separating molecules by molecular sieve and affinity chromatography.

4. Indicate the experimental methods which are used to determine the N-terminal and the C-terminal amino acid residues in a protein.

EXERCISES

1. How is the native structure of a protein or enzyme defined?

2. What are the forces which take part in determining the following level of protein structure?
   a. Primary
   b. Secondary (α-helix and β-pleated sheet)
   c. Tertiary
   d. Quaternary

3.   Write out the equation for the reaction of β—mercaptoethanol with a protein.

4.   Explain how the following reagents will specifically denature proteins.
    a.   Urea
    b.   Lowering the pH to 2
    c.   Increasing the salt concentration from physiological concentration (0.15 M NaCl) to 1.0 M NaCl.

5.   Write the equation for the reaction of the reagent or enzyme listed below with the peptide, ala-trp-met-his-lys. Show the structure for the modified amino acid, if one is produced.
    a.   Phenylisothiocyanate
    b.   BrCN
    c.   Trypsin
    d.   Chymotrypsin

6.   A protein of 200 amino acid residues occurs naturally in a completely α-helical arrangement. By altering the solution conditions, it is converted to a parallel β—sheet arrangement in which one molecule interacts side-by-side with another.
    a.   What is the length of the α-helix and the β-pleated sheet?
    b.   In the conversion of the α-helix to the β-pleated sheet, is the length of the protein increased or decreased?

7.   Upon the addition of O_2 to a solution of either myoglobin (Mb) or hemoglobin (Hb), the Fe^{+2} is said to undergo **oxygenation** and not **oxidation**. Explain.

8.   Consider the following experimental techniques used to separate a mixture of proteins.
    a.   Affinity chromatography
    b.   Electrophoresis
    c.   Molecular sieve chromatography
    d.   Paper chromatography
    e.   Anion exchange chromatography
    f.   Isoelectric focusing
    g.   SDS-PAGE

Indicate the physical basis for separating a mixture of proteins by each technique and indicate which protein would be the first to elute from the column or have the greatest migration in the gel or paper?

9.   X-ray crystallography has played an especially significant role in our understanding of the structural and mechanistic aspects of biomacromolecules.
     a.   What particle in the atom is responsible for the scattering of the X-rays and producing the diffraction pattern?
     b.   In a protein such as myoglobin, which has N, C, O, H, Fe, and S atoms, what is the relative intensity of the scattering from each of these atoms?

10.   Hemoglobin is a multisubunit protein which binds four molecules of O_2 in a cooperative manner.
     a.   How is this expressed in terms of the K (binding constants) and ΔG^0 values for O_2 binding?
     b.   Suggest a mechanism by which this cooperativity might occur.

11.   After carrying out a number of separation procedures to isolate a pure enzyme, an investigator performed an enzymatic assay on a solution of the purified fraction and was elated to find that the fraction exhibited a high enzymatic activity. In order to be thorough and add further support to his feeling of finally achieving success, the investigator analyzed the protein fraction by SDS-PAGE and isoelectric focusing (IEF). The results are shown below. How do you interpret these data?

12.   Indicate which of the following statements is true or false. If the statement is false, correct it.

    a.   The heme group in each subunit of hemoglobin is covalently bound to the protein by the Fe^{+2}.
    b.   Molecular oxygen binds to myoglobin in a non-cooperative manner and exhibits a sigmoidal binding curve.
    c.   Decreasing the solution pH from pH 7.6 to 7.2 will increase the O_2 binding in hemoglobin.
    d.   In the supersecondary structure referred to as $\beta\alpha\beta$, the β-pleated sheets are in a parallel arrangement.
    e.   The Bohr effect refers to the influence that O_2 binding has on the binding of CO_2 in hemoglobin.
    f.   The binding of H^+ to hemoglobin alters the quaternary structure of hemoglobin.

ANSWERS TO EXERCISES

1.   The native structure is defined as that structural arrangement which exhibits optimum biological activity.

2.   a.   Covalent (peptide) bonds connect each amino acid residue in the primary structure.
    b.   Hydrogen bonds involving the atoms in the peptide backbone (not the side chains) are involved in secondary structure.
    c. and d.   Virtually all the non-covalent forces are involved in the tertiary and quaternary structure of a protein. These include hydrogen bonds, electrostatic interactions and hydrophobic interactions.

3.   β-Mercaptoethanol reacts with cystines in a protein to reduce them. This involves the breaking of the disulfide bond.

$$
\begin{array}{cccc}
 & \text{Reduced} & \text{Oxidized} & \\
2\,HSCH_2CH_2OH + & \underset{\substack{|\ \ | \\ S\text{-}S}}{\text{Protein}} & = & \underset{\substack{|\ \ | \\ HS\ \ SH}}{\text{Protein}} + HOCH_2CH_2S\text{-}SCH_2CH_2OH
\end{array}
$$

4.   a.   Urea is a molecule which very effectively forms hydrogen bonds in solution. Therefore, if added in high concentration to a protein solution, it will compete with and disrupt the hydrogen bonds which were (in part) responsible for maintaining the protein in its native structure. The structure of urea is shown below. The oxygen and the nitrogen atoms can act as hydrogen bond acceptors, while the hydrogens act as hydrogen bond donors.

$$\begin{array}{c} O \\ \parallel \\ H_2N - C - NH_2 \end{array}$$

b.   A solution at pH 2 will be very acidic and protonate many groups, such as glutamic acid and aspartic acid. This will change the character of the carboxyl groups and disrupt electrostatic interactions which may have been structurally important under normal pH conditions.

c.   Increasing the salt concentration will disrupt the electrostatic interactions in the protein.

5.   a.   Phenylisothiocyanate reacts with the amino-terminal residue of the pentapeptide. Upon hydrolysis, a tetrapeptide and the modified N-terminal amino acid, alanine, in the form of a phenylthiohydantoin alanine, will be produced.

+   trp-met-his-lys

b.   BrCN will react with the methionine residue, cleave the peptide bond on the carboxyl side and produce a tripeptide and dipeptide. The methionine residue is modified to a homoserine lactone (cyclic ester) in the process.

+   his-lys

87

c.   Trypsin cleaves a peptide at the carboxyl side of a lysine or arginine residue. Since the lysine residue is the C-terminal residue in this peptide, trypsin will have no effect on it.

d.   Chymotrypsin will cleave on the carboxyl side of an aromatic residue, such as tryptophan. Therefore, it will yield a dipeptide and a tripeptide.

ala-trp   +   met-his-lys

6.   a.   The axial distance between adjacent amino acid residues in an α-helix is 1.5 A and that for a β-pleated sheet is 3.5 A. Therefore, the lengths for the two types of secondary structure are:

α-helix: (199) x (1.5 A) = 298.5 A

β-pleated sheet :   (199) x (3.5 A) = 696.5 A

b.   The α-helix is a very compact form of secondary structure, while the β-pleated sheet arrangement is much more extended. The structural conversion results in an increase in the length of the protein by more than a factor of two.

7.   The iron in both myoglobin and hemoglobin is in the plus two oxidation state, Fe^{+2}. It is essential for the functioning of both proteins that the iron remain in the ferrous state. This is accomplished in the protein, primarily by the way in which the heme group is positioned within the architecture of the protein. As a result, oxygenation occurs (the binding of the molecule O_2), instead of oxidation in which there would be a transfer of electrons, resulting in the conversion of Fe^{+2} to the Fe^{+3} state. It is known that if the iron is oxidized to Fe^{+3}, both myoglobin and hemoglobin do not bind O_2 and therefore the proteins lose their essential activity.

Oxidation: Fe^{+2} (ferrous) + O_2 ----> Fe^{+3} (ferric)

Reversible oxygenation: Fe^{+2} + O_2 = Fe^{+2}-(O_2)

8.   a.   Only proteins which exhibit a high affinity for a specific substrate will bind. The substrate is covalently bound to the column material. All the proteins which have no affinity for the substrate elute first, while the proteins which binds strongly and specifically to the

bound substrate are retained. A typical example of this would be a column in which an antibody to a specific protein (A) is covalently bound. If a mixture of proteins were loaded on the column, all proteins would readily elute from the column, with the exception of the protein A. Protein A could then be eluted from the column under (different) elution conditions which would disrupt the interaction between the antibody and protein A.

b.   Proteins would migrate according to their charge. Proteins with the greater charge exhibit a greater mobility. The sign of the charge would determine the direction of migration, with the positively charged species migrating toward the negative pole, while the negatively charged species would migrate toward the positive pole.

c.   Proteins separate according to size. Smaller proteins become trapped in the sieves and therefore they are retarded in the elution. The larger proteins are excluded from the sieves and are eluted at early times. The largest proteins elute first.

d.   This technique is generally not used for proteins, but is valuable for small molecules and peptides. The molecules separate according to polarity. The mobile phase is less polar than the stationary phase and therefore the relative mobility of the molecules parallel their solubility in the non-polar or less-polar phase. Non-polar molecules exhibit the greater mobility.

e.   An anion exchange column is positively charged and interacts electrostatically with charged species. The column binds anionic species, in which molecules having the greater number of negatively charged groups exhibit the highest affinity. Species which are positively charged, or do not interact with the positively charged groups on the column material, are the first to elute.

f.   Isoelectric focusing separates proteins according to their characteristic pI value (i.e., the pH at which the protein has a net zero charge). Experimentally, this is an electrophoretic (gel) separation in a continuous pH gradient. If the protein mixture is loaded on the end of the gel which has a high pH, the the proteins with the lowest value of pI will exhibit the greatest migration.

g.   Proteins are separated by size under denaturing conditions in SDS-PAGE. The smallest protein will exhibit the greatest mobility.

9.   a.   X-rays are scattered by the electrons in the atom.

   b.   The scattering intensity is proportional to the number of electrons in the atom. Therefore, the relative scattering intensity for the atoms in myoglobin would be: $Fe \gg S > O > N > C > H$.

10.   a.   Hemoglobin contains four subunits, each containing a heme group. Each heme group contains an Fe^{+2}, which binds one molecule of O_2. The first O_2 has the most difficulty binding to Fe^{+2}. This means that its binding constant (K_1) is the smallest. The second O_2 binds more strongly (i.e., K_2 is greater than K_1). This trend continues until the four molecules of O_2 are bound. Since the successive K_n values increase, the corresponding ΔG^0 values become progressively more negative.

   b.   Since the binding of the four O_2 molecules occurs on four different subunits, there must be a form of "molecular communication" between the subunits. The binding of the first O_2 alters the tertiary structure of the subunit to which it is bound. This change in the tertiary structure results in a change in the molecular contacts between the individual subunits. This effects a change in the tertiary structure of the second subunit, which enhances the binding of O_2 to this subunit. As a result, an overall change in the quaternary structure of the protein is produced. This continues on until hemoglobin is saturated with four molecules of O_2.

11.   The SDS-PAGE data indicate that there is a protein of about 40,000 Daltons. Our friend is feeling confident and is ready to send out invitations for a party.
   Ouch! Wait a minute! The IEF gel, however, reveals that there are two species, with individual pI values of 6.4 and 7.4.
   These data bring out a potential caveat in SDS-PAGE. The **presence of a single band does not mean the presence of only one protein** in the sample. It could mean that there is (1) one protein in the sample (2) multiple proteins with the essentially the same molecular weight or (3) one protein, but with a post-translational modification such as a phosphate group (or a number of other groups) added onto an amino acid residue. Such modifying groups usually have small molecular weights and add relatively little to the total molecular

weight of the protein, such that the migration is indistinguishable from that of the unmodified protein. Since other interpretations are also possible, further experiments must be carried out before the investigator can claim success. This example emphasizes that before success is declared, a number of different properties of the protein must be examined and all must be consistent with the presence of a single, unique protein.

12.   a.   True.
     b.   False.   A sigmoidal curve is a characteristic feature of cooperative binding in a protein.
     c.   False.   Decreasing the pH will decrease the extent of O_2 binding to hemoglobin.
     d.   True.
     e.   False.   The Bohr effect refers to the influence of the binding of H^+ and CO_2 on O_2 binding in hemoglobin.
     f.   True.

The Behavior of Proteins: Enzymes

For life to exist as we know it, biological reactions must proceed at tremendous rates, with high specificity and with no side reactions. Enzymes, which are the catalysts in living organisms, serve this essential role. Substrates interact specifically with the enzyme in the region called the active site and are converted into products. The binding interaction can be described either by the lock-and-key or the induced-fit models. The kinetic analysis of enzyme catalyzed reactions can be understood by the Michealis-Menten kinetic model, which assumes the intermediate formation of an enzyme-substrate complex. The enzymes can be characterized by their K_M and V_{max} values, both of which can be obtained by plotting velocity as a function of substrate concentration in a Lineweaver-Burk double reciprocal plot. Molecules which reversibly inhibit enzyme activity can be experimentally classified as either competitive or noncompetitive inhibitors. Allosteric or regulatory enzymes have multiple subunits and exhibit more complex kinetics as a result of cooperative interactions and the effects from the binding of allosteric effectors. In most cases, the behavior of allosteric interactions can be described adequately by either the concerted or the sequential models. An alternate mechanism used to regulate enzyme activity involves the specific cleavage of the backbone in zymogens to activate enzymatic activity in the product molecule. The mechanism or pathway by which an enzyme catalyzed reaction takes place is directly linked to the amino acid residues in the active site. The architecture of the active site and the interactions between the amino acid residues and the substrate weaken or strain the appropriate substrate bond. In a wide variety of these reactions, a coenzyme directly participates in one or more steps in the conversion of substrate to product.

CHAPTER OBJECTIVES

1.   Distinguish between the spontaneity and the rate of a reaction and indicate what factors determine each characteristic.

2.   Indicate how a reaction mechanism differs from the overall equation which describes the reactants and products.

3.   Describe the nature of the active site in an enzyme when a substrate interacts by 1) the lock-and-key and 2) the induced-fit model.

4.   Outline the features of enzymes which display a hyperbolic or alternatively, a sigmoidal reaction profile.

5.   For enzymes which follow the Michaelis-Menten kinetic model, derive the expression, $V = V_{max}[S]/(K_M+[S])$, and explain how this leads to a first order and zero order reaction at low and high substrate concentrations, respectively.

6.   Discuss the significance of K_M and V_{max} values for an enzyme.

7.   Describe the enzyme interactions involved with competitive and noncompetitive (reversible) inhibitors and the associated equilibrium expressions.

8.   Indicate the characteristic differences in the Lineweaver-Burk plots as a result of a competitive and a noncompetitive inhibitor interacting with an enzyme.

9.   Compare the allosteric behavior of hemoglobin (Hb) and aspartate transcarbamoylase (ATCase) and indicate the homotropic and heterotropic effectors in each case.

10.   List the distinguishing features of the concerted and the sequential models which are used to describe allosteric enzymes.

11.   State the definition of a zymogen and indicate several specific enzymes in which this strategy for the regulation of enzymatic activity is used.

12.   List the amino acid residues that are able to play a direct role in the catalytic action of an enzyme.

13. Indicate the species or groups in an enzyme molecule that participate in general acid-base and Lewis acid-base catalysis and how they can specifically stimulate the reaction rate.

14. Indicate what characterizes a coenzyme and describe how coenzymes participate in catalysis.

EXERCISES

1. What is the effect of a catalyst on the values of ΔG^0 and $\Delta G^{0\ddagger}$?

2. The rate equation for a reaction is: Rate $= k [A]^1[B]^0$.

    a. Indicate the order of the reaction for A and B and the overall order of the reaction.

    b. If the reaction rate is determined to be 0.5 M/sec. when $[A] = 0.01M$ and $[B] = 0.67M$, calculate the value of the rate constant.

3. Chymotrypsin has 28 serine residues. However, reaction with diisopropylphosphofluoridate produces only one covalently modified serine residue. Explain.

4. Consider the diagram below which shows the reaction profile for a catalyzed and uncatalyzed reaction. Label the coordinates of the plot, in addition to labeling the diagram appropriately with ΔG^0, $\Delta G^{0\ddagger}_{forward}$, and $\Delta G^{0\ddagger}_{reverse}$ for both the catalyzed and uncatalyzed reactions.

5.   a.   The rate constant of an enzymatic reaction depends on what fundamental parameters?
      b.   The rate of an enzymatic reaction depends on what parameters?

6.   An enzyme which has its maximum activity at pH 5.0 exhibits a greatly reduced activity at pH 7. Briefly explain.

7.   Reactions in organic and inorganic chemistry typically proceed faster as the temperature is increased. This same trend is observed when an enzyme catalyzed reaction is carried out at 15, 25 and 40^0C. However, at 45^0C and 50^0C, the reaction rate decreased sharply. Provide an explanation for this observation.

8.   The value of K_M for the enzyme was determined to be $1 \times 10^{-6}M$. A competitive inhibitor is added to this enzyme catalyzed reaction.
      a.   What affect does the inhibitor exert on the the value of K_M and V_{max}?
      b.   If the inhibitor concentration is $1 \times 10^{-7}M$ and K_M apparent (the K_M value determined in the presence of the inhibitor) was determined to be $1 \times 10^{-3}M$, what is the value for K_I?

9.   A number of enzymes are found to conform to an induced-fit model.
      a.   What can be said about the conformation of the enzyme, at or immediately in the vicinity of the active site, before and after the interaction with a substrate?
      b.   What experimental technique can be used to support this proposition? How would the experiment be carried out?

10.   Aspartate transcarbamoylase (ATCase) is an allosteric enzyme. It is involved in the first step in pyrimidine synthesis. Both CTP and ATP serve as allosteric effectors, which respectively inhibit and activate the enzyme.
      a.   Explain how this serves to efficiently regulate this pathway in nucleotide biosynthesis.
      b.   It is found that if p-hydroxymercuribenzoate reacts with ATCase, the allosteric properties of the enzyme are lost. However, the substrates bind to the enzyme in a noncooperative fashion and the enzyme exhibits catalytic activity. Explain.

11.   It has been proposed that for enzymes which obey Michaelis-Menten kinetics, the K_M value for an enzyme may represent the approximate physiological substrate concentration in the cell. Examine a typical plot of V versus [S] and explain why this appears to be a reasonable suggestion.

12.   Indicate whether the following statements are true or false. If the statement is false, correct it.

   a.   The V_{max} value is a fundamental characteristic for each enzyme.

   b.   Enzymes which conform to Michealis-Menten kinetics are not involved in any feedback regulation.

   c.   Enzymes reduce the value of ΔG^0 more than that of $\Delta G^{\ddagger}$ for a reaction.

   d.   The formation of an intermediate, enzyme substrate complex is a basic assumption in the Michealis-Menten model.

   e.   Substrates can be bound to the active site of the enzyme by either covalent or non-covalent interactions.

   f.   The K_M value for an enzymatic reaction is always an indication of how tightly the binding is between the substrate and the enzyme.

   g.   A molecule, such as diisopropylphosphofluoridate, which covalently binds within the active site of serine proteases, is an example of an effective competitive inhibitor.

   h.   The acid, HCl, can act as a general acid catalyst.

   i.   The clotting of blood provides an elegant example of how the activation of zymogens play a critical part in a multistep process.

   j.   Allosteric enzymes always exhibit sigmoidal plots of V versus [S].

   k.   The sequential model for an allosteric enzyme assumes that the R and the T forms of the enzyme are in equilibrium.

   l.   The greater the association constant, K_M, for the ES complex, the stronger the interactions between the enzyme and the substrate.

ANSWERS TO EXERCISES

1.   A catalyst has no effect on the free energy difference between the reactants and the product, ΔG^0. On the other hand, a catalyst decreases the value of $\Delta G^{0\ddagger}$, the activation energy required to bring the reactants to the transition state. Refer to Figure 10.1a in the text.

2.   a.   The reaction is first order for [A], zero order for [B] and first order overall.

b.

$$\text{Rate} = 0.5 \text{ M/sec.} = k\ (0.01\ M)^1 (0.67\ M)^0$$
$$= 0.5 \text{ M/sec.} = k\ (0.01\ M)$$
$$\underline{k = 50 \text{ sec}^{-1}}$$

3.   This type of selective hyperreactivity is quite common in enzymes and indicates that the one serine is in a unique environment which makes it especially reactive relative to the others. The reactive residue is found in the active site.

4.

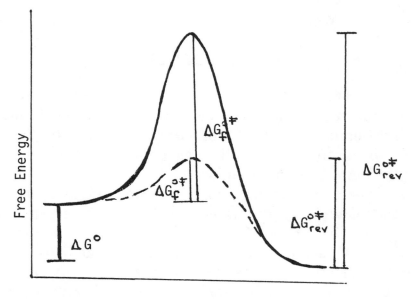

Reaction Profile

5.   a.   The <u>rate constant</u> for an enzymatic reaction depends on the temperature and the $\Delta G^{0\ddagger}$ value.

b.   The rate of the reaction depends on the rate constant and the solution conditions, such as the concentration of substrate, pH, etc.

6.   Enzymes are generally very sensitive to the pH of the solution. This is because the acidic or basic amino acid residues can become protonated or deprotonated as the pH changes. Since the character of the amino acids influences the native structure of the enzyme, and especially the nature of the active site, the catalytic activity is often strongly influenced by pH.

7.   Enzymes are sensitive to the temperature of the solution because their secondary and tertiary (and if a multisubunit enzyme, the quaternary) structure is determined by a multitude of weak non-covalent interactions. At some point, as the temperature is increased, these forces will be sufficiently disrupted that the native structure is altered and the catalytic activity is reduced or completely lost.

8.   a. V_{max} is unchanged by a competitive inhibitor, while the apparent K_M value is increased by the factor $(1 + [I]/K_I)$.

b. $$K_{M \text{ apparent}} = K_M(1 + [I]/K_I)$$

$$\underline{K_I = 1 \times 10^{-10} M}$$

9.   a.   Enzymes which can be described by the induced fit model have a conformation which is not complementary to that of the substrate. The conformation will change in and about the active site as a result of the substrate binding.

b.   Isolate a crystal of the enzyme with and without bound substrate and determine the structure by X-ray crystallography. The structures would be expected to be different in and about the active site of the enzyme. In actual practice, it is not possible to obtain the structure of an enzyme interacting with a true, intact substrate. Therefore, a competitive inhibitor or a modified substrate is used in place of the substrate.

10a. CTP is the final product in this pathway. It acts as a feedback allosteric inhibitor as it binds to an effector site (different and distinct from the substrate site) to reduce the activity of ATCase. ATP, on the other hand, is not involved directly in this pathway and is an allosteric activator. Since ATP and CTP bind to the same effector site, they will compete with each other. The effector that binds will depend on the relative concentrations of each effector and their respective binding constants. The reason that ATP exerts an effect on this pathway is because both ATP and CTP are needed for RNA and DNA synthesis. The role of ATP is to aid in coordinating the production of pyrimidine nucleotides with that for purine nucleotides. It is even further complicated in that ATP is also required as the cellular source of energy.

     b.   P-hydroxymercuribenzoate binds to ATCase to dissociate the subunits. The substrates can continue to bind and the enzyme exhibits activity, but it has lost its allosteric and regulatory character.

11.   The V versus [S] plot is shown on the right for a simple enzyme obeying Michealis-Menten kinetics. The K_M value represents the substrate concentration at 1/2(Vmax). The proposal suggests that if the [S] were significantly less than this value, most of the enzyme activity would be, in effect, unused and therefore, 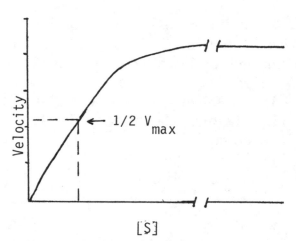 wasted. On the other hand, if the [S] in the cell were twice as large or much larger than the K_M value, the enzyme would be saturated and small changes in the [S] would not effect the rate of the reaction. With the [S] at approximately the value of K_M, much of the enzymatic activity is being used. If the concentration of substrate within the cell were to change, the rate of the catalyzed reaction would change accordingly, so that some degree of regulation would be effected by changing metabolic states.

12.

    a.   False. V_{max} is not really a fundamental characteristic of an enzyme. It depends on the <u>conditions</u> which are used to carry out the reaction (i.e., the amount of enzyme and substrate).

    b.   True.

    c.   False.   Enzymes do not affect the ΔG^0 value.

    d.   True.

    e.   True.

    f.   False.   This is only true under conditions in which $k_{-1} > k_2$.

    g.   False.   Competitive inhibitors, and also noncompetitive inhibitors, must interact reversibly with the enzyme by noncovalent interactions.

    h.   False.   General acid catalysis requires the reversible donation and acceptance of a proton from a weak acid.

    i.   True.

    j.   True.

    k.   False.   Only the T form of the allosteric enzyme exists. The binding of an effector induces a conformational change from the T to the R form.

    l.   False. K_M is a <u>dissociation</u> constant for the ES complex, as shown below. The smaller the K_M value, the stronger the binding is in the [ES] complex.

$$ES = E + S \qquad K_M = ([E][S])/[ES]$$

11

The Dynamics of Membrane Structure

Biological membranes serve as actively functioning envelopes about both the cell and the organelles within. These molecular assemblies provide both the means for communicating with other cells in unicellular and multicellular organisms (or between organelles in a eukaryotic cell) and the mechanisms by which ions, nutrients, waste products and even macromolecules enter and leave these metabolizing units. The basic components of all membranes are simply lipid bilayers. However, a mosaic of structural and functional variations exists between organelles and between cells from different tissues. These variations are due to the presence of different lipid molecules, functional protein receptors, transport proteins and gated-channels associated with the bilayer, all of which contribute to making the molecular assembly a functioning biological membrane for a living cell.

CHAPTER OBJECTIVES

1. Draw the structures for a glycolipid and a phosphoglyceride and indicate why they are considered amphiphilic.
2. Describe the lipid bilayer model for a membrane.
3. Name and draw the molecules which make up the membranes of animal cells and indicate their relative orientation within the bilayer.
4. Indicate what factors contribute to the fluidity of a lipid bilayer or a biological membrane.
5. Describe how a cooperative structural transition (ordered to disordered) occurs when thermal energy is added to a membrane.
6. Explain the difference between lateral and "flip-flop" or transverse diffusion of lipids in a membrane and indicate the relative probability of each.
7. Outline the characteristics of peripheral and integral proteins and indicate some important functions they perform in the membrane.
8. Describe the fluid mosaic model for a biological membrane.
9. Distinguish between passive, facilitated and active transport mechanisms for the movement of molecules and ions from one side of the membrane to the other.
10. Generally characterize a membrane receptor and indicate an example of how this relates to a specific medical problem.
11. Describe the difference between a ligand-gated and a voltage-gated channel and explain how they may be involved in a neuromuscular junction.

EXERCISES

1. Acquired immune deficiency syndrome (AIDS) is a disease which is caused by the viral infection of cells associated with the development of an immune response. The so-called helper T cells, involved in cellular immunity, are the ones which are specifically infected. Suggest a reason for the apparent specificity of the HIV (Human Immunodeficiency Virus) for these T cells.

2.   Consider the accompanying composite drawing of the cell, which shows some molecules or ions which must be transported into or out of the cell or one of the organelles. For each small molecule, indicate whether the transport process involves:

    a.   passive transport
    b.   facilitated transport
    c.   active transport

In each case, indicate whether the process is a spontaneous one (i.e., a decrease in the free energy, $-\Delta G$, for the process).

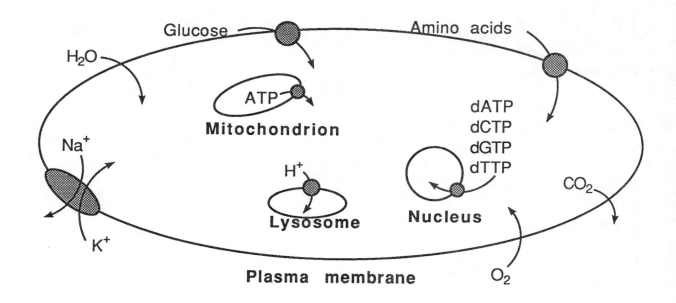

A Collection of a Few Transport Systems in Most Cells

3.   The free energy change that occurs when an uncharged species at concentration, c_1, is transported from side 1 to side 2, where it is at concentration, c_2, is given by the equation:

$$\Delta G = 2.303 \, RT \log [c_2]/[c_1]$$

    a.   If the concentration of $c_1 > c_2$, is the process spontaneous?
    b.   If the concentration of $c_1 < c_2$, is the process spontaneous?
    c.   Consider the situation in which the glucose concentration outside the cell is 20 mM and that inside the cell is 20 uM (micromolar).

103

What is the free energy change for the transport of glucose into the cell at 37⁰C?

~assign for Kinetics chapter

4. The kinetic profile for the transport of ethanol (a) and glucose (b) across a cell membrane is shown in the following Figure. Explain these profiles in terms of the mechanisms by which these two molecules are transported across a membrane. The concentrations of the molecules outside and inside the cell are c_1 and c_2, respectively.

a.

b.

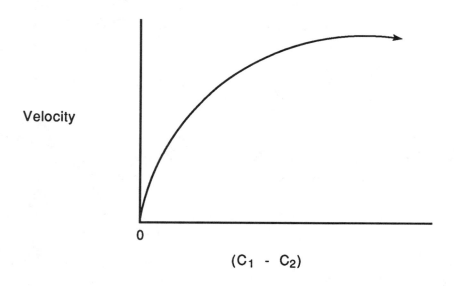

5. The data in the Table below show the K_M values for the transport of a number of sugars by the erythrocyte glucose transport protein across a red blood cell membrane.

    a. What is the definition of the K_M value?

    b. Interpret these findings.

Sugar	K_M Value
D-glucose	1.5 mM
L-glucose	>3000 mM
D-mannose	20 mM
D-galactose	30 mM

6.   a. Describe what is meant by lateral motion and the "flip-flop" or transverse motion of lipids in a bilayer.

    b. What is the relative probability of lipids in a membrane undergoing each of these motions.?

7. Indicate what information can be obtained from electron micrographs of cell membranes which have been freeze-fractured.

8. The communication between nerves and muscles at the neuromuscular junction involves both voltage and ligand gated channels.

    a. Which ions in the nerve cell are involved in this signal transmission?

    b. Which ions take part in this process in the muscle cell?

    c. Name the molecule involved in the ligand-gated channel which is essential for nerve transmission. Draw its structure and point out its functional groups.

    d. After the binding of the neurotransmitter to the ligand-gated channel (receptor) and the postsynaptic cell is depolarized, the molecule must very quickly leave the receptor so that the receptor can return to its original state and continue taking part in subsequent nerve impulses. This is accomplished by the hydrolysis of acetylcholine by the enzyme, acetylcholinesterase. At which bond does this enzyme act and what are the resulting products?

    e. The molecule, succinylcholine, shown below, is used as a muscle relaxant. Suggest a reason for its effectiveness.

$$(CH_3)_3\overset{+}{N}-CH_2-CH_2-O-\overset{\overset{O}{\|}}{C}-CH_2-CH_2-\overset{\overset{O}{\|}}{C}-O-CH_2-CH_2-\overset{+}{N}(CH_3)_3$$

ANSWERS TO EXERCISES

1.   The specificity of the HIV virus for T cells is due to the presence of receptor proteins, called CD 4 receptors, on the surface of the T cells. The first step in the infection is the binding of the virus to the cell surface. This binding occurs through the specific interaction of the HIV virus with the CD 4 receptor, a large transmembrane protein.

2.   The Figure shows a variety of molecules which are transported into or out of the cell or an organelle. The transport of the ions and molecules can be cataloged accordingly;

Passive Transport - random and simple diffusion through a lipid bilayer membrane, primarily involving H_2O and small non-polar molecules.
This would include the molecules, CO_2 and O_2. This transport is a spontaneous process involving no input of energy.

Facilitated Transport - transport which occurs only with the assistance of a specific membrane carrier protein, often called a permease or translocator protein.
The molecules which are associated with this type of transport are glucose and amino acids. In these cases, the molecules diffuse from a compartment of high concentration to one of a lower concentration. Therefore, there is no expended energy and the transport is spontaneous.

Active Transport - specific molecules or ions are transported from low concentration to high concentration, against a concentration gradient. This is a facilitated transport process also, but it requires the input of energy. This is not a spontaneous process.
Both the K^+ and Na^+ ions are pumped into and out of the cell, respectively, against a concentration gradient by the Na^+-K^+ pump. This multisubunit transmembrane protein, referred to as the Na^+-K^+ ATPase, links the transport of Na^+ and K^+ ions, in that it pumps three Na^+ ions out, for every two K^+ ions pumped into the cell. This occurs with the concomitant hydrolysis of ATP to provide the energy to make this an exergonic process.
The H^+ also undergoes active transport into the lysosomes since its concentration is much higher in the lysosomes than in the cytoplasm.

In the case of glucose transport, in which there is transport of only a single molecule across a membrane, the mediated transport process is called **UNIPORT**. In the case of the Na^+-K^+ ATPase, the transport is referred to as an **ANTIPORT**, because two different molecules or ions are simultaneously transported in opposite directions.

For the ATP transport (an anionic species) out of the mitochondrion, a transport protein has been isolated, but the process is not well characterized at this time. Whether it involves a facilitated transport requiring energy is yet to be resolved.

The mechanism of transport of the deoxyribonucleotides (dATP, etc) into the nucleus is likewise not firmly understood at this time. An interesting feature of the nuclear membrane is that it has relatively huge "pores" which permit the transport of large molecules in and out of the nucleus. Because of the unusual size of these pores, it is quite possible, but not certain, that passive transport may be involved in this process.

These last two cases emphasize that biochemistry is an ongoing venture in which many important questions are still being addressed and answers are being earnestly sought. Our efforts are only beginning to give us a more comprehensive understanding of the functioning of the cell.

3.   a.   Since this process involves the transport of a species from a side at high concentration to one at a lower concentration, the process is spontaneous and the ΔG will be negative.

b.   The situation is just the opposite when $c_2 > c_1$. In this case, the process would involve the transport of a species from a side with a lower concentration to the side with a higher concentration. This is not a spontaneous process and ΔG will be positive. This process will only occur if there is an input of useful energy from another source.

c.

$$\Delta G = 2.303 \, RT \log [C_{in}]/[C_{out}]$$

$$\Delta G = 2.303 \, (8.31 \text{ J/mol-K}) (310^0 K) \log [20 \text{ uM}/ 20{,}000 \text{ uM}]$$

$$\underline{\Delta G = -17.8 \text{ kJ/mol}} \qquad \text{This is a spontaneous process.}$$

4.   The profiles indicate that the mechanism of transport is different for the two molecules. The kinetic characteristics for the transport of ethanol is a classic profile for **simple diffusion**. The greater the concentration gradient across the membrane, the greater will be the diffusion rate.

On the other hand, the transport of glucose exhibits quite different characteristics. This profile is analogous to that of Michaelis-Menten kinetics for reactions being catalyzed by simple (non-allosteric) enzymes. Recall that the Michaelis-Menten kinetic model assumes the interaction of a substrate with the enzyme to produce the enzyme-substrate complex, ES, which then dissociates to product and enzyme.

$$S + E = ES \longrightarrow product + E$$

This profile then suggests an analogous process for glucose transport in which glucose must interact with a transport protein to facilitate its transport across the membrane. At low concentrations of glucose, the kinetics are linear since there is an abundant supply of transport protein to readily facilitate transport of all the glucose. However, as the glucose concentration increases, the amount of transport protein becomes comparable to that of glucose and the kinetics are no longer strictly linear. At very high concentrations, there is no change in the transport velocity as the glucose concentration increases. This indicates that the transport protein is limiting and what is there, is completely saturated. Note that an effective V_{max} and K_M can be obtained for the transport process by an analysis which utilizes a Lineweaver-Burk plot.

This is the characteristic profile found for cases in which the transport is by **facilitated diffusion.** One final point; although glucose can be transported through a membrane by simple diffusion also, the mechanism of facilitated diffusion predominates because it is so much more efficient. For glucose, facilitated diffusion provides a transport mechanism which is about a factor of 500 greater than that for simple diffusion.

a.

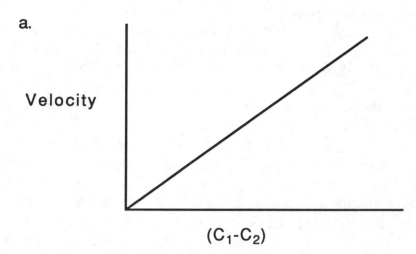

Velocity

$(C_1 - C_2)$

b.

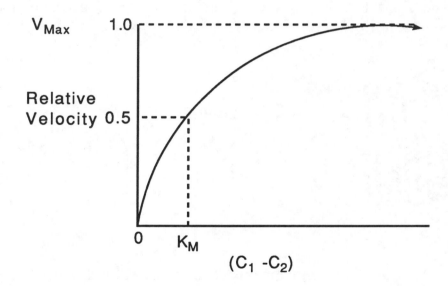

V_{Max} 1.0

Relative
Velocity 0.5

0   K_M

$(C_1 - C_2)$

Plots of initial rates of diffusion
versus concentration difference

5.   a.   The K_M value is the concentration value at which the transport velocity occurs at one-half the maximum rate. It is an expression of the "goodness-of-fit" of the substrate for the permease or transport protein, being analogous to the K_M value in enzyme kinetics. The LOWER the value for K_M, the better the fit and the more proficient the transport process.

   b.   The data indicate that D-glucose has the lowest K_M value of the four sugars studied. The value is many orders of magnitude lower than that for the L form of glucose (an enantiomer) and more than one order of magnitude over that for either mannose or galactose. These latter two monosaccharides are epimers of glucose (they differ in the configuration at only one asymmetric center). These data therefore emphasize the important point that the transport protein for glucose is highly specific for the molecule it transports. This is similar to the characteristics for enzymes, in which the enzymes are highly specific for the substrates upon which they act. This finding of specificity for a molecule can be regarded as a general characteristic for other transport proteins.

6.   a.   The lipid bilayer is often referred to as being made up of two "leaflets" of phospholipid molecules.

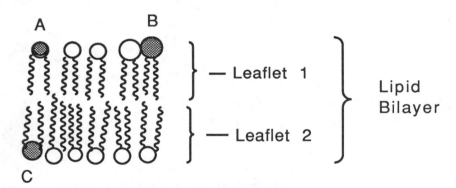

Lateral motion is the movement of a phospholipid from one region of a leaflet to another region in the **same leaflet** (the movement of the molecule in position A to position B). On the other hand, traverse or "flip-flop" motion involves the **transfer of a phospholipid from one leaflet to the other leaflet** (the movement of the molecule at position A to position C).

   b.   The probability of these two different motions is very different because of the energetics involved in each process.

Lateral movement is energetically favorable and therefore very rapid (occurs continuously). It involves the movement of the molecules in their same orientation, keeping the polar head groups on the outside of

110

the bilayer, interacting favorably with the aqueous environment, while the non-polar tails remain in the interior, interacting with other non-polar tails.

Transverse or "flip-flop" diffusion of a phospholipid molecule requires the movement of the polar head group through the non-polar regions. This is energetically unfavorable and therefore a relatively rare event.

7.   Freeze-fracture of a cell membrane opens up and separates the membrane such that the inner side of the leaflets (the non-polar tails) can be examined. A granular appearance indicates that there are integral proteins in the membrane.

8.   a.   The ion in the nerve cells is Ca^{+2}.
      b.   The ions in the muscle cells are Na^+ and Ca^{+2}.
      c.   Acetylcholine, which contains both an ester and an (quaternary) amine functionality, is shown below.

$$\begin{array}{c} O \\ \| \\ CH_3 - C - O - CH_2 - CH_2 - \overset{+}{N}(CH_3)_3 \end{array}$$

      d.

Ester Linkage

$$CH_3 - \overset{\overset{O}{\|}}{C} - O - CH_2CH_2 - \overset{+}{N}(CH_3)_3 \xrightarrow{AC} CH_3 - \overset{\overset{O}{\|}}{C} - OH + HO - CH_2CH_2 - \overset{+}{N}(CH_3)_3$$

Acetic acid   Choline

AC = acetylcholinesterase

e.   Succinylcholine is a structural analog of acetylcholine, which is a competitive inhibitor of acetylcholinesterase. It competes for the active site, and although it is hydrolyzed by acetylcholinesterase, this occurs at a much slower rate than acetylcholine. This results in a longer depolarization and muscle contraction is inhibited.

Metabolism and Electron Transfer

Metabolism can generally be considered as the breakdown of foods that are ingested to provide energy and the fundamental building blocks for the (bio)synthesis of biomolecules required to sustain life. Although many types of reactions are involved, catabolism is an oxidative process which liberates energy, while anabolism is a reductive process which requires the input of energy. Coenzymes, such as NADH, NADPH, $FADH_2$ and their oxidized forms, serve as electron donors and acceptors. Together with molecules such as ATP, which contain "high energy" bonds, these small molecules act as essential partners in many of the enzymatic reactions. In many metabolic pathways, endergonic reactions are coupled to exergonic reactions, with the latter providing the thermodynamic driving force for a thermodynamically favored, coupled reaction. The essential role of ATP and molecules taking part in electron transfer will become vividly clear as the processes of glycolysis, the citric acid cycle and oxidative phosphorylation are explored in subsequent chapters.

CHAPTER OBJECTIVES

1.   Discuss the relationship between catabolic and anabolic processes in cellular metabolism.

2.   Indicate the fundamental differences between processes which are catabolic or anabolic, specifying if the process is exergonic or endergonic and whether the molecules of interest are undergoing oxidation or reduction.

3.   Provide a number of equivalent definitions for both oxidation and reduction.

4.   Make a list of the most important biological electron acceptors; draw their structures and point out the part of the molecule which is altered by the reduction.

5.   List the most important biological electron donors; draw their structures and indicate the part of the molecule which is altered as a result of oxidation.

6.   Explain the meaning of the term "high energy" bond.

7.   Draw the structure for ATP; point out the acid anhydride and the ester linkages and indicate the high energy bonds.

8.   Indicate the number of electrons and protons that NADH, NADPH and $FADH_2$ transfer when they are oxidized.

9.   Discuss how the coupling of an endergonic reaction to an exergonic reaction can produce an overall reaction which is thermodynamically favored.

10.   Draw the structure for coenzyme A (CoA); point out the recognizable components in its chemical structure and indicate the role of CoA in metabolism.

11.   List the three important processes in the metabolism of glucose and indicate whether they are anaerobic or aerobic.

EXERCISES

1.   Indicate the oxidant and the reductant in both the reactants and products for each of the reactions below. If there is no oxidation or reduction, indicate no redox reaction is occurring.

114

a. $ATP + H_2O = ADP + P_i$

b. Glyceraldehyde 3-phosphate $+ P_i + NAD^+ =$ 1,3-bisphosphoglycerate $+ NADH + H^+$

c. $6 H_2O + 6 CO_2 = C_6H_{12}O_6 + 6 O_2$

d. $Mg + CuCl_2 = MgCl_2 + Cu$

e. $2 H_2O_2 = 2 H_2O + O_2$

2. Match the terms in the left column with the appropriate word or phrase in the right column.

a. $FADH_2$ _____

b. ATP _____

c. Acetyl-CoA _____

d. Catabolic process _____

e. NAD^+ _____

f. CoA _____

g. Endergonic process _____

h. Oxidation _____

i. Anabolism _____

j. CoA, FAD^+, NADH _____

1. Exergonic, oxidative process

2. Exhibits a positive ΔG

3. Transfers 2 H^+ and 2 e^-

4. Contains both ester and acid anhydride bonds

5. Removal of hydrogens

6. High energy thioester

7. Has a reactive sulfhydyl group

8. An oxidizing agent

9. Has ADP in its structure

10. Biosynthesis

115

3. An endergonic reaction (a) having a ΔG^0 of 20 kJ/mol is coupled to an exergonic reaction (b) which has a ΔG^0 of -52 kJ/mol. Calculate the equilibrium constant at 25^0C for each individual reaction and the coupled reaction.

4. The reaction in which glucose is converted to lactate and 2 H^+ has a ΔG^0 value of -196 kJ/mol. Consider the coupling of this reaction to the reaction for the production of ATP, in which 2 ATPs are produced. What is the standard free energy for the coupled reaction?

5. In the up-coming chapters, cellular metabolism will be presented in terms of the catabolic and anabolic reactions in the cells. The metabolic pathways will include glycolysis, the citric acid cycle, electron transport and oxidative phosphorylation, fatty acid synthesis and more. As alluded to in Chapter 1, catabolic processes produce ATP, the universal energy carrier, while anabolic processes utilize ATP in the biosynthesis of macromolecules. In this complex array of interrelated processes, each pathway is regulated in a number of ways. One of the more important regulatory signals in the cell is the level of ATP.

An expression of the energy state of the cell is the **energy charge**. It is the mole fraction of the adenosine nucleotides in the cell which have high-energy phosphates. The expression is:

Energy charge = {[ATP] + 1/2[ADP]}/ {[ATP] + [ADP] + [AMP]}

The ADP concentration is multiplied by 1/2 because it has only 1/2 the number of high-energy bonds found in ATP. This ratio can theoretically vary from 1.0 (fully charged) to 0 (completely discharged). The analogy of the cellular energy charge to an automobile battery is often made. The energy charge in the cell, however, is held within a limited range, at about 0.9.

In order to regulate the energy charge in the cell, ATP and ADP are allosteric effectors of regulatory enzymes in a number of the pathways. One such regulatory enzyme in the catabolic glycolysis pathway is phosphofructokinase.

a. What is the energy charge when the [ATP] = 4mM, [ADP] = 1mM and the [AMP] = 0.15mM?

b. What type of effectors are ATP and ADP on phosphofructokinase and what effect would each exert on the production of ATP and the energy charge?

6. Draw the structures for coenzyme A and the oxidized and reduced forms of the coenzymes, NAD^+ and FAD. Indicate the reactive sites in each molecule.

ANSWERS TO EXERCISES

1. a. This is a hydrolysis reaction, not a redox reaction.

    b. Glyceraldehyde 3-phosphate and NADH are reducing agents and therefore will be oxidized. NAD^+ and 1,3-bisphosphoglycerate are oxidizing agents and will be reduced. Any reaction which involves NAD^+/NADH or $FAD/FADH_2$ are redox reactions.

    c. H_2O and $C_6H_{12}O_6$(glucose) are oxidized, while CO_2 and O_2 are reduced.

    d. Mg and Cu will be oxidized, while $CuCl_2$ and $MgCl_2$ are reduced.

    e. In this reaction, the reactant, hydrogen peroxide, **disproportionates** to H_2O and O_2. That is, the reactant undergoes both a self-oxidation and reduction. Therefore, H_2O_2 and O_2 are reduced, while H_2O_2 and H_2O are oxidized.

2.

a.	3		f.	7
b.	4		g.	2
c.	6		h.	5
d.	1		i.	10
e.	8		j.	9

3. Reaction a. $\Delta G^0 = 20$ kJ/mol.

$$\Delta G^0 = -2.303 \ RT \log K$$
$$20,000 \ J/mol = -2.303 \ (8.31 \ J/mol^{-1} \ K^{-1}) \ (298^0 K) \log K$$
$$\log K = -3.5$$
$$\underline{K = 3 \times 10^{-4}}$$

Reaction b. $\Delta G^0 = -52$ kJ/mol

117

$$\log K = 9.1$$
$$\underline{K = 1 \times 10^9}$$

According to Hess's Law, thermodynamic state functions, such as G, H and S for reactions, can be simply added to obtain the quantity for the coupled or resultant combined reaction.

Coupled Reaction with $\Delta G^0_{total} = \Delta G^0_1 + \Delta G^0_2$
$$= 20 \text{ kJ/mol} + (-52 \text{ kJ/mol})$$
$$= -32 \text{ kJ/mol}$$

$$\log K = 5.61$$
$$\underline{K = 4 \times 10^{\pm 5}}$$

By coupling reactions (a) to (b), the equilibrium constant for the reaction increases by 9 orders of magnitude.

4.   The individual reactions of interest are:

Glucose	$= 2 \text{ Lactate}^- + 2 \text{ H}^+$	$\Delta G^0_1 = -196 \text{ kJ/mol}$
$\text{ATP} + \text{H}_2\text{O}$	$= \text{ADP} + \text{P}_i$	$\Delta G^0_2 = +30 \text{ kJ/mol}$

The overall reaction is:
$$\text{Glucose} + 2 \text{ ATP} + 2 \text{ H}_2\text{O} = 2 \text{ Lactate}^- + 2 \text{ ADP} + 2 \text{ P}_i + 2 \text{ H}^+$$

The overall free energy for the reaction is:

$$\Delta G^0_{overall} = \Delta G^0_1 + 2 \Delta G^0_2$$

$$= -196 + 2(+30)$$
$$= \underline{-136 \text{ kJ/mol}}$$

This shows that the reaction for glycolysis (glucose to lactate) is an exergonic reaction which can be used to produce 2 molecules of ATP and remain an exergonic reaction.

5.   a.   Energy charge = (4mM + 0.5mM)/(4mM + 1mM + 0.15mM)

Energy charge = 0.87

b.　The glycolysis pathway is associated with the oxidation of glucose and is catabolic in character. It is involved in the generation of ATP. When ATP levels are low and ADP levels are high, ADP interacts with phosphofructokinase to increase the activity of this enzyme and as a result increaase the level of glycolysis and ATP production. ADP is therefore an positive allosteric effector. The increased level of ATP will increase the energy charge. On the other hand, when ATP levels are high, ATP acts as an negative effector and interacts with phosphofructose to inhibit its activity. The allosteric effectors, ADP and ATP, are regulators of metabolism.

6.　a.

Coenzyme A (CoA)

b.

The reduced and oxidized forms - NADH and NAD⁺

c.

Oxidized form of FAD

Reduced form of FADH$_2$

The reactive region is shown with the carbon and nitrogen atoms in the larger type.

13

Glycolysis: Anaerobic Oxidation of Glucose

Glycolysis represents one of the most primitive pathways and the singularly most important exergonic pathway for the catabolism of glucose not only in man, but also in plants and many microorganisms. It involves the stepwise conversion of monosaccharides, primarily glucose, to pyruvate. In the process, energy is released, with part of it being converted into useful work in living organisms. Under anaerobic conditions, pyruvate may then be reduced to lactate or ethanol (alcoholic fermentation). On the other hand, under aerobic conditions, pyruvate loses CO_2, reacts with coenzyme A to produce acetyl-CoA and then shuttles into the citric acid cycle. The main storage form of glucose, glycogen, is a polymer of glucose, which can serve as a readily available energy source. Enzymatic digestion of glycogen produces glucose, which is subsequently incorporated into the glycolysis pathway. The **pentose phosphate pathway** provides an important alternate route to glucose metabolism. This pathway generates five carbon sugars, in addition to the reducing agent, NADPH, which is essential in subsequent reductive biosynthesis reactions. **Gluconeogenesis** is the exergonic process in which pyruvate is converted to glucose. The process is the reverse of glycolysis except for three points in the glycolytic pathway where the reactions are essentially irreversible. Alternate routes are used at these points for glycolysis and gluconeogenesis. These reactions are of particular importance since they regulate the catabolic and anabolic pathways, with the regulation mechanisms acting in a reciprocal manner (i.e., when glycolysis is active, gluconeogenesis is inactive).

CHAPTER OBJECTIVES

1. State the primary function of the glycolysis pathway.
2. Outline the steps involved in the conversion of glucose to pyruvate.
3. Indicate the types of reactions involved in glycolysis, if the reaction involves the production or use of ATP, and whether the reaction is exergonic or endergonic.
4. Indicate the enzymes which catalyze each reaction in glycolysis and point out the enzymes which take part in the regulation of glycolysis.
5. Indicate the allosteric effector(s) for each regulatory enzyme and the effect that is produced by the interaction.
6. Write out the reactions for an aldol condensation and Schiff base formation and present an example of each reaction as it occurs in glycolysis.
7. Specify the difference between substrate-level phosphorylation and phosphorylation involving ATP.
8. Outline the mechanism for the conversion of glyceraldehyde 3-phosphate to 1,3-bisphosphoglycerate by glyceraldehyde 3-phosphate dehydrogenase.
9. Specify the alternate metabolic fates of pyruvate and indicate under what conditions they may occur.
10. Indicate to what extent the energy released by the oxidation of glucose in glycolysis is "captured" and into what molecular form this is.
11. Explain how glycogen is broken down so it can enter the glycolytic pathway and how the overall energetics of the oxidative process are different from those involved in only glycolysis.
12. Outline the mechanistic role of the cofactor, thiamine pyrophosphate (TPP), in the enzymatic decarboxylation of pyruvate by pyruvate decarboxylase.
13. Specify the biological role of the pentose phosphate pathway.
14. List the types of reactions involved in the (oxidative) conversion of glucose 6-phosphate to ribulose 5-phosphate in the pentose phosphate pathway.

15. Indicate the general group transfer roles of transketolase and transaldolase in the nonoxidative phase of the pentose phosphate pathway.
16. Draw the structure for thiamine pyrophosphate and indicate the role of this coenzyme with transketolase.
17. State the role of gluconeogenesis.
18. Indicate the three reactions and the associated enzymes in the gluconeogenesis pathway which are different from those in glycolysis.
19. Explain the role of the coenzyme, biotin, with pyruvate carboxylase.
20. Under anaerobic conditions due to oxygen debt in skeletal muscles, discuss the interrelationship between liver and muscle cells and the metabolic interconversions of glucose, lactate and glycogen.

EXERCISES

1. What are the final products of glucose metabolism in the following cells? In each case, write the equation showing the overall reaction.
    a. In actively metabolizing cells with a plentiful supply of O_2.
    b. In muscle cells of the leg after a strenuous 440 yard dash.
    c. In yeast cells under anaerobic conditions.

2. Consider the molecules and the reactions in the anaerobic glycolytic pathway.
    a. How many carbon atoms are in the intermediate molecules?
    b. In a number of cases, the intermediate molecule is simply modified in a reaction. Considering this, what is the minimum number of "parent" molecules (C_n units) which are intermediates in the pathway.
    c. Comparing the standard free energies in Table 13.1 (text) for the reactions in the glycolysis pathway, indicate which reactions are highly exergonic?
    d. Of the ten reactions in glycolysis, how many actually involve an oxidation of an intermediate? Write out these reactions.
    e. Oxidations in which O_2 **is directly** involved are catalyzed by enzymes classified as either **oxygenases** or **oxidases**. In cases in which oxidations occur in the absence of O_2, what is an alternate way of producing an oxidation?

3.   Indicate the redox reactions which are in the "oxidative phase" of the pentose phosphate pathway? Write out the reactions.

4.   The primary function of the pentose phosphate pathway is to generate (1) NADPH for subsequent reductive biosynthesis and (2) ribose 5-phosphate for the synthesis of nucleotides.
a.   At what points in the pathway have these primary functions been accomplished?
b.   Sum up the individual reactions involved in the production of these two molecules and write the final net equation.

5.   a.   List the coenzymes involved in reactions discussed in this chapter?
      b.   Name at least one enzyme which requires each coenzyme for activity.
      c.   What is the essential function of each coenzyme?
      d.   Draw the structure of each coenzyme and indicate the reactive site.

6.   What molecules are common to both glycolysis and the pentose phosphate pathway and therefore fix the interrelationship between the two pathways?

7.   Cellular glutathione can reduce disulfide bonds in proteins. Write the general equation for this non-enzymatic reaction.

8.   Write the reaction for the reduction of oxidized glutathione by NADPH.

ANSWERS TO EXERCISES

1.   In all three cases, glucose will be converted via the 10 steps in the glycolytic pathway to pyruvate. After this point, the fate of the pyruvate will depend on the presence or absence of molecular O_2 and on the organism involved.
      a.   In actively metabolizing muscle cells, each pyruvate molecule loses one CO_2 and each remaining C2 unit (acetyl) is linked to coenzyme A to produce acetyl-CoA. This enters the citric acid cycle and becomes oxidized to two molecules of CO_2 (i. e., derived from the acetyl group). Upon completion of oxidative

phosphorylation, the glucose has been completely oxidized to CO_2 and water.

$$C_6H_{12}O_6 + 6\,O_2 \;\longrightarrow\; 6\,CO_2 + 6\,H_2O \qquad \Delta G^{0'} = -2870 \text{ kJ/ mol}$$

b.   After a strenuous run, the muscle cells of the leg will be deficient in O_2 and therefore, aerobic oxidation of pyruvate does not take place. In this environment, pyruvate will be **REDUCED** to lactate. Under these conditions, known as anaerobic glycolysis, lactate will be the terminal product.

$$C_6H_{12}O_6 \;\longrightarrow\; 2 \text{ lactate}^- + 2\,H^+ \qquad \Delta G^{0'} = -196 \text{ kJ/mol}$$
$$(C_3H_5O_3)$$

c.   In yeast cells, the pyruvate is decarboxylated to acetaldehyde (loss of CO_2) and the acetaldehyde is then **REDUCED** to ethanol (aldehyde reduced to an alcohol).

$$C_6H_{12}O_6 \;\longrightarrow\; 2 \text{ ethanol} + 2\,CO_2 \qquad \Delta G^{0'} = -167 \text{ kJ/mol}$$
$$(C_2H_5OH)$$

All three processes (reactions) are exergonic. However, there is incomplete oxidation of of glucose in the anaerobic conditions. In these conditions, the amount of energy liberated is less than 7% of that for the aerobic condition, in which the glucose is completely oxidized.

2.   a.   There are intermediate molecules which have either 6- or 3-carbon atoms.
      b.   For C6, the molecules are glucose and fructose. For C3, the molecules are dihydroxyacetone, glyceraldehyde, glycerate and pyruvate.
      c.   There are only 4 reactions which are highly exergonic. They are:

i. glucose + ATP ---> glucose 6-phosphate + ADP   -16.7

ii. fructose 6-phosphate + ATP --> fructose 1,6 bisphosphate   -13.8
                                                    + ADP

iii. 1,3-bisphosphoglycerate + ADP ---> 3-phosphoglycerate   -37.6
                                                    + ATP

iv. phosphoenolpyruvate + ADP ---> pyruvate + ATP   -62.8

d. Of the 10 reactions, only one reaction is an oxidation. The reaction is:

glyceraldehyde 3-phosphate + NAD^+ + P_i ----->
    1,3-bisphosphoglycerate + NADH + H^+

Since NAD^+ is reduced to NADH, the other reactant must be oxidized.

e. The oxidation in question 2d involves the transfer of a hydrogen from the substrate to NAD^+. Alternate descriptions for an oxidation include the loss of a hydrogen atom or the loss of electrons.

3. The first three reactions in the pentose phosphate pathway are considered the "oxidative phase". Of the three reactions, only the first (an oxidation) and the third (an oxidative decarboxylation) are oxidative, with $NADP^+$ serving as the oxidizing agent.

glucose 6-phosphate + $NADP^+$ = NADPH + 6-phosphoglucono-δ-lactone
                                                + H^+

6-phosphogluconate + $NADP^+$ = NADPH + ribulose 5-phosphate
                                                + CO_2 + H^+

4.   a.   The primary function is accomplished after the isomerization of ribulose 5-phosphate. The synthesis of NADPH has been accomplished in reactions 1 and 3 in the "oxidative phase".

      b.   The net reaction for the production of these molecules is:

glucose 6-phosphate + 2 NADP⁺ =   ribose 5-phosphate + CO_2
                                                                  + 2 NADPH + 2 H^+

5.   a, b, c.

Coenzyme	Enzyme(s)	Function
NAD^+	Many dehydrogenases (ex., glyceraldehyde 3-phosphate dehydrogenase)	Acts as an oxidizing agent (e⁻ acceptor)
NADH	Lactate dehydrogenase	Acts as a reducing agent (e⁻ donor)
$NADP^+$	Glucose 6-phosphate dehydrogenase	Acts as an oxidizing agent (e⁻ acceptor)
TPP	Transketolase	Cleavage or formation of a carbon-carbon bond adjacent to a carbonyl carbon
Biotin	Pyruvate decarboxylase	A CO_2 carrier; Carboxylation or Transcarboxylation

d.

The reduced and oxidized forms of NADPH and NADP$^+$

In NADH and NAD$^+$, the circled phosphate group
is replaced with a hydroxyl group (-OH).

Thiamine pyrophosphate (TPP)

Biotin

6. glucose 6-phosphate, fructose 6-phosphate, glyceraldehyde 3-phosphate.

7.

$$2 \ \gamma\text{-glu-cys-gly} \ + \ \text{Protein} \ = \ \gamma\text{-glu-cys-gly} \ + \ \text{Protein}$$

$$\underset{\textbf{SH}}{|} \qquad \underset{\textbf{S - S}}{| \quad |} \qquad \underset{\textbf{S}}{|} \qquad \underset{\textbf{SH \quad SH}}{| \quad |}$$

$$\underset{\textbf{S}}{|}$$

$$\underset{\gamma\text{-glu-cys-gly}}{|}$$

8.

$$\gamma\text{-glu-cys-gly}$$

$$\underset{\textbf{S}}{|}$$

$$\underset{\textbf{S}}{|} \quad + \ NADPH + H^+ \ \xrightarrow[\longleftarrow]{\text{--------}} \ 2 \ \text{glu-cys-gly} \ + \ NADP^+$$

$$\underset{\gamma\text{-glu-cys-gly}}{|} \qquad\qquad\qquad\qquad \underset{\textbf{S H}}{|}$$

Oxidized form   Reduced form

This reaction proceeds far to the right in most cells.

14

The Citric Acid Cycle

The citric acid cycle serves as the hub of cellular metabolic activity. It provides the central oxidative pathway by which metabolic fuel molecules - the carbohydrates, amino acids and fatty acids - are catabolized and energy, in the form of ATP, is generated under aerobic conditions. In addition, the metabolic intermediates serve as precursors for the biosynthesis of such diverse molecules as proteins, lipids and the heme group. Acetyl-CoA, the intermediate formed by the breakdown of the fuel molecules, serves as the dominant "entry molecule" to the cycle. As a result of the eight reactions in the cycle, the acetate group is oxidized to two molecules of CO_2 and three molecules of NADH, one molecule of $FADH_2$ and one GTP is produced. The NADH and $FADH_2$ molecules will be subsequently oxidized in the electron transport chain by O_2 to generate additional ATP molecules. Regulation within the cycle occurs at three points involving the enzymes, citrate synthase, isocitrate dehydrogenase and α-ketoglutarate. In addition, the activity of pyruvate dehydrogenase is under stringent control. Each of the four reactions associated with these enzymes exhibits a large negative $\Delta G^{0'}$ value, which is a general characteristic of a regulatory step. All of the reactions associated with the citric acid cycle take place in the matrix of the mitochondria. The glyoxylate cycle, found only in plants and some microorganisms, is a variant of the citric acid cycle and provides a unique route to carry out the net synthesis of carbohydrates from fat.

CHAPTER OBJECTIVES

1.   State the primary catabolic and anabolic roles of the citric acid cycle and indicate the cellular location of the process.
2.   Write the individual enzymatic reactions of the citric acid cycle, indicating which reactions are exergonic.
3.   Write out the overall reaction for the conversion of pyruvate to CO_2.
4.   Name and draw the structures of the intermediates for the citric acid cycle.
5.   List the enzymes associated with each reaction in the citric acid cycle and indicate the type of reaction which is taking place.
6.   Indicate the regulatory enzymes in the cycle and the small molecules which are inhibitors and activators for these allosteric enzymes.
7.   List the components of the multienzyme complex, pyruvate dehydrogenase.
8.   For the conversion of pyruvate to acetyl-CoA, write the five stepwise reactions involved and specify the enzymes and the coenzymes associated with each intermediate conversion.
9.   Write out the reactions involved in the glyoxylate cycle and state the importance of this cycle in plant cells.

EXERCISES

1.   Name the di- and tricarboxylic acids that are in the citric acid cycle.

2.   Pyruvate dehydrogenase and α-ketoglutarate dehydrogenase are both multienzyme complexes which require multiple coenzymes and a number of reactions to catalyze the conversion of pyruvate and α-ketoglutarate, respectively, to their products. These enzymes accomplish this by very similar mechanisms. Suggest a reason for this observation.

133

3. Name the enzymes in the citric acid cycle and indicate the type of reaction that each catalyzes.

4. Acetyl-CoA is an example of a thioester. It has a $\Delta G^{0'}$ value for hydrolysis of -31.5 kJ/mol, while a typical $\Delta G^{0'}$ value for an ordinary ester is about -15-20 kJ/mol.
  a. Draw the structure for a simple thioester and an ordinary ester.
  b. Write the reaction for the hydrolysis of each type of ester.
  c. Explain why the standard free energy of hydrolysis is so much greater for the thioester than for an ordinary ester.

5. In Table 14.1 (text), the reaction for the conversion of malate to oxaloacetate has a $\Delta G^{0'}$ value of +29.2 kJ/mol, indicating that this reaction is not spontaneous and has no thermodynamic driving force. However, the reaction takes place in the cell. Propose an explanation for this apparent anomaly.

6. In the reaction in which succinyl-CoA is converted to succinate, one molecule of GTP is produced. It is stated that the production of GTP is equivalent to that for ATP. How can you explain this in light of the following exchange reaction?

$$GTP + ADP = GDP + ATP$$

7. Indicate whether the following statements are true. If false, correct the statement.

  a. Pyruvate dehydrogenase catalyzes the reversible conversion of pyruvate to acetyl-CoA.
  b. The reactions in the citric acid cycle take place in the matrix of the mitochondria.
  c. Pyruvate must be transported into the mitochondria before it can be acted upon by pyruvate dehydrogenase.
  d. Lipoic acid is covalently attached to arginine by an amide linkage in the multienzyme, pyruvate dehydrogenase complex.
  e. Lipoic acid can act as both an oxidizing agent and an acyl group acceptor.
  f. The initial reaction in the citric acid cycle and the glyoxylate cycle involves the formation of a carbon-carbon bond.

134

g.   Thiamine pyrophosphate (TPP) is a coenzyme involved in the two oxidative decarboxylation reactions in the citric acid cycle.

h.   The conversion of citric acid to isocitrate is necessary because citric acid cannot be oxidized, while isocitrate is readily oxidized.

i.   After the completion of the citric acid cycle, in which glucose has been converted to 6 molecules of CO_2, virtually all of the energy and ATP have been produced.

8.   a.   Draw a general diagram for the citric acid cycle and the glyoxylate cycle and show the intermediates. Explain briefly the important and the different features of each cycle.

b.   Where does the glyoxylate cycle take place in plant cells?

c.   Why can fat be metabolized to produce **net** carbohydrate synthesis in the glyoxylate cycle, but not in the citric acid cycle?

d.   Write out the net equation for the reaction taking place in the glyoxylate cycle.

e.   Why isn't acetyl-CoA simply not converted to pyruvate to produce a pathway for the net synthesis of carbohydrate?

f.   Name and draw the structure for any molecules which are unique to the glyoxylate cycle.

9.   a.   What are the enzymes within the citric acid cycle which will regulate the cycle according to metabolic needs?

b.   When a cell is in a metabolic state in which the ATP and the NADH levels are high, what can be said about the metabolic activity associated with the citric acid cycle?

ANSWERS TO EXERCISES

1.   Tricarboxylic acids: Citric acid
                                  Isocitric acid
        Dicarboxylic acids: α-Ketoglutaric acid
                                  Succinate
                                  Fumarate
                                  Malate
                                  Oxaloacetate

2.   Both reactions are similar in that they involve an oxidative decarboxylation of an α-keto acid to an acyl thioester.

     a.   pyruvate   ----->   acetyl-CoA

$$H_3C-\overset{\overset{\displaystyle O}{\|}}{C}-COO^- + CoA\text{-}SH \longrightarrow H_3C-\overset{\overset{\displaystyle O}{\|}}{C}-S\text{-}CoA + CO_2$$

     b.   α-ketoglutarate   ----->   succinyl-CoA

$$^-OOC-CH_2-CH_2-\overset{\overset{\displaystyle O}{\|}}{C}-COO^- + CoA\text{-}SH \longrightarrow {}^-OOC-CH_2-CH_2-\overset{\overset{\displaystyle O}{\|}}{C}-S\text{-}CoA + CO_2$$

3.

Enzymes	**Reaction Type**
1. Citrate synthetase	Condensation
2. Aconitase	Isomerization (Note that this results from a hydration reaction followed by a dehydration reaction).
3. Isocitrate Dehydrogenase	Oxidative Decarboxylation
4. α-Ketoglutarate Dehydrogenase	Oxidative Decarboxylation
5. Succinate Thiokinase	Hydrolysis and Phosphorylation
6. Succinate Dehydrogenase	Dehydrogenation (i.e., oxidation)
7. Fumarase	Hydration
8. Malate Dehydrogenase	Dehydrogenation (i.e., oxidation)

(The numbers refer to the reactions in the Figure for the citric acid cycle in the answer to question 8).

4. a. The structures for a simple thioester and an ordinary ester are shown below.

$$R - C - S - R'$$
Thioester

$$R - C - O - R'$$
Ester

b.

$$RC-SR' + H_2O \longrightarrow RC-O^- + R'-SH$$

$$RC-OR' + H_2O \longrightarrow RC-O^- + R'-OH$$

c. The $\Delta G^{0'}$ for the reaction is the difference between the free energy of the products and the reactants. This $\Delta G^{0'}$ is primarily a result of the difference in the resonance stabilization of the ester compared to the thioester. Because of the comparable sizes of the carbon and oxygen atoms (and the p orbitals in these atoms), there will be a resonance stabilization in the ester. This is produced by the favorable overlap in the resulting π-orbital or electron overlap in the ester. Because the sulfur atom is larger than the carbon atom, there is little or no stabilization energy in the thioester. The resonance forms are shown below.

Resonance between the
two forms

Little or no resonance
between the two forms

The stabilization energy lowers the energy of the ester relative to the thioester. The product molecules in both cases have comparable energies. The carboxylate anions are, in fact, the same. Therefore, the $\Delta G^{0'}$ between the ester and carboxylate anion is smaller than the $\Delta G^{0'}$ for the

137

thioester and carboxylate anion. This corresponds to the energy of hydrolysis being smaller for the ester.

The following Figure shows the proposed differential overlap in a (CO) and a (CS) bond.

Generalized picture of π- orbital overlap

Ester   **Thioester**

5.   The positive value for the standard free energy change for this reaction indicates that it is clearly very unfavorable. The reaction within the cell is not at standard conditions. This factor, in addition to the influence of the subsequent reaction in the cycle, must be considered. The following reaction is for the condensation of acetyl-CoA and oxaloacetate, which is highly exergonic. This reaction depletes the concentration of oxaloacetate continuously during active metabolism and in this way, helps to drive the reaction to the right.

6.   The production of GTP is equivalent to that for ATP because the exchange reaction has a $\Delta G^{0'}$ of zero. This indicates that there is effectively free exchange between the nucleoside diphosphate and nucleoside triphosphate (NDP and NTP) species.

7.
   a.   False.   This reaction is essentially irreversible.
   b.   True.
   c.   True.
   d.   False.   Lipoic acid is attached to a lysine residue.
   e.   True.

f.   True.

g.   False.   In the citric acid cycle, only the reaction for the conversion of α-ketoglutarate to succinyl-CoA uses TPP as a coenzyme. The oxidative decarboxylation of isocitrate does not. The conversion of pyruvate to acetyl-CoA also uses TPP, but this reaction is not in the citric acid cycle. Note, however, that the two reactions which utilize TPP are associated with the oxidative decarboxylation of α-keto acids (pyruvate and α-ketoglutarate).

h.   True.   Recall that citric acid is a tertiary alcohol and does not undergo oxidation, while isocitrate is a secondary alcohol and readily undergoes oxidation. Refer to the summary of organic reactions in chapter 4 in this book.

i.   False.   Most of the molecules of ATP generated from the oxidation of glucose will be derived indirectly from the reoxidation of the NADH and $FADH_2$ molecules in the electron transport chain and oxidative phosphorylation.

8.   a.   In plants, fatty acids are produced as a result of the breakdown of lipids. The fatty acids are further catabolized to two carbon (acetyl) units and the acetyl-CoA is funnelled into the glyoxylate cycle. As shown in the Figure below, reactions 1 and 2, and the enzymes that catalyze these reactions, are the same as in the citric acid cycle. Isocitrate is the product after these first two reactions. However, **reactions 3 to 7 are not part of the glyoxylate cycle.** Therefore, reactions 3 and 4, which eliminate two molecules of CO_2, are by-passed in the glyoxylate cycle. Isocitrate undergoes a cleavage reaction (**A**), catalyzed by isocitrate lyase, to produce glyoxylate and succinate. The glyoxylate undergoes a condensation reaction (**B**) with another molecule of acetyl-CoA to produce malate. This reaction is catalyzed by malate synthase. The malate then undergoes dehydrogenation (8) to produce oxaloacetate, which is then ready to initiate another turn of the citric acid or glyoxylate cycle. Note that there are only **five reactions in the glyoxylate cycle** (reactions 1, 2, **A**, **B** and 8).

The succinate which was produced in the glyoxysomes is transported to the mitochondria and there enters the citric acid cycle, where reactions 6 to 8 are carried out to complete the cycle. Since there is now an additional succinate molecule (four carbon unit) introduced into the citric acid cycle, once it is converted to oxaloacetate, it can be readily used in carbohydrate synthesis via gluconeogenesis.

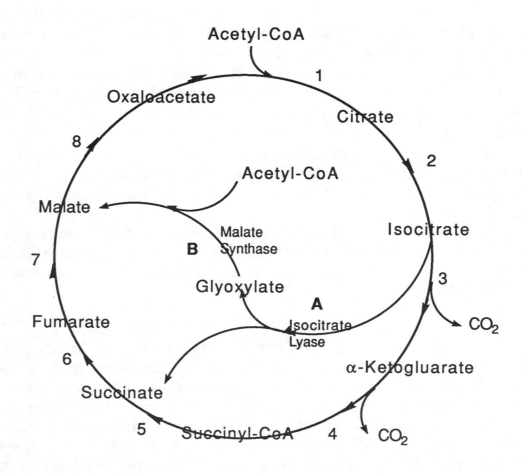

b.   The glyoxylate cycle takes place in the glyoxysomes of plant cells.

c.   Net carbohydrate synthesis from fat can be carried out in the glyoxylate cycle because there is a net synthesis of a four-unit carbon, succinate, in this cycle, This does not occur in the citric acid cycle. The succinate then shuttles to the mitochondria and into the citric acid cycle, where there is now an additional succinate per turn of the cycle. This can then be used for carbohydrate synthesis.

d.   The net equation for the glyoxylate cycle is:

$$2 \text{ acetyl-CoA} + \text{NAD}^+ \longrightarrow \text{succinate} + \text{NADH} + \text{H}^+ + 2 \text{ CoA-SH}$$

e.   The conversion of pyruvate to acetyl-CoA, which is catalyzed by pyruvate dehydrogenase, is an irreversible reaction. The reverse reaction, conversion of acetyl-CoA to pyruvate, does not take place.

f.   Glyoxylate is the only molecule unique to the glyoxylate cycle. It is a two carbon molecule with the following structure:

$$COO^-$$
$$|$$
$$O=C-H$$

9.   a.   Regulation of the citric acid cycle is accomplished by the following three enzymes:

Citrate synthetase
Isocitrate dehydrogenase
α-Ketoglutarate dehydrogenase

Notice that the regulation of the cycle occurs at reactions which have a large and negative value for the standard free energy change (i.e., spontaneous reactions).

b.   In cells which have high levels of ATP and NADH levels, the citric acid cycle will be inhibited since ATP and NADH will act as allosteric inhibitors on the regulatory enzymes.

15

Electron Transport and Oxidative Phosphorylation

The catabolic pathways for proteins, carbohydrates and lipids culminate cellular respiration with electron transport and oxidative phosphorylation in the mitochondria. In the complete oxidation of one mole of glucose by molecular O_2, CO_2 and H_2O are produced with the liberation of 2823 kJ/mol of energy. In the process, 24 electrons are transferred indirectly from glucose to oxygen and much of the energy is captured and used for the synthesis of ATP from ADP and phosphate. The mechanism involves the exergonic and step-wise transfer of electrons from the reduced coenzymes, NADH and $FADH_2$, through the electron transport chain. Three major multienzyme complexes which are located in the mitochondrial inner membrane, are key molecular assemblies in the respiratory chain. The use of respiratory inhibitors, which obstruct the transfer of electrons at specific sites in the chain, was instrumental in defining the order of the electron carriers in the membrane. The final enzyme in the chain, cytochrome oxidase, ultimately transfers the electrons to the final electron acceptor, molecular oxygen. The chemiosmotic coupling theory provides the most widely accepted mechanism to explain the coupling of this electron transport to the oxidative phosphorylation process. It proposes that the enzymes in the electron transport chain are also involved in pumping hydrogen ions from the matrix into the intermembrane space to create a proton gradient. It is this gradient which then provides the thermodynamic driving force for the phosphorylation of ADP by the multisubunit enzyme complex, ATP synthetase.

CHAPTER OBJECTIVES

1. Indicate the cellular location where glycolysis, the citric acid cycle, electron transport and oxidative phosphorylation take place.

2. Specify the role of $FADH_2$, NADH and O_2 in the electron transport chain.

3. State the relationship between the reduction potential (E^0) and the capability of a chemical species to act as a reducing agent.

4. Define the relationship between the standard free energy ($\Delta G^{0'}$), the standard reduction potential ($\Delta E^{0'}$) and the equilibrium constant for a reaction.

5. Name the three multienzyme complexes, the proteins and cofactors in each complex and the order in which the multienzyme complexes are found in the electron transport chain.

6. Indicate the electron-carriers which serve to transfer electrons between the multienzyme complexes in the electron transport chain.

7. Characterize the multisubunit ATP synthetase, identify its location in the cell and its roles in oxidative phosphorylation.

8. Define the terms uncouplers and respiration inhibitors, and indicate the general mechanism by which each operates.

9. Discuss the basic tenets of the chemiosmotic hypothesis which proposes a mechanism for the coupling of electron transport to oxidative phosphorylation; indicate experimental findings which support this hypothesis.

10. Outline the basic ideas in the conformational coupling mechanism for coupling electron transport to oxidative phosphorylation.

11. Describe the two shuttle mechanisms by which electrons from NADH are transported from the cytoplasm into the mitochondria.

12. Review the cytoplasmic and mitochondrial reactions involved in the complete oxidation of glucose and indicate the reactions which result in the production of ATP, NADH and $FADH_2$.

143

EXERCISES

1. Consider the list of half-reactions below. Indicate which molecule has the following characteristic.

Redox Couple	$E^{0'}$ (V)
Succinate + CO_2 + 2 H^+ + 2 e^- ----> α-ketoglutarate + H_2O	-0.67
Oxaloacetate + 2 H^+ + 2 e^- ----> malate	-0.17
Fumarate + 2 H^+ + 2 e^- ----> succinate	-0.03

    a.   The best reducing agent   _____

    b.   The best oxidizing agent: _____

    c.   Will be most readily reduced: _____

    d.   Will be most readily oxidized: _____

2. The $E^{0'}$ value for the overall reaction in the oxidation of NADH by molecular oxygen is +1.14 volts. This corresponds to the voltage as a pair of electrons move through the entire electron transport chain. The equation for the reaction is written below.

$$NADH + H^+ + 1/2\ O_2\ ----> \ NAD^+ + H_2O \qquad E^{0'} = 1.14\ V.$$

    a.   Calculate the $\Delta G^{0'}$ value and the equilibrium constant for this reaction.

    b.   The oxidation of one mole of NADH in respiration produces 3 moles of ATP. What is the efficiency of the oxidative phosphorylation process under standard conditions?

3. Indicate the molecular species in the inner membrane of the mitochondria which serve as proton pumps or channels.

4.   The molecule, 2,4-dinitrophenol, is an effective uncoupling agent.

    a.   What effect does it produce in the electron transport chain and on the production of ATP?

    b.   Suggest a possible mechanism for this process.

    c.   If a laboratory rat is given 2,4-dinitrophenol, both its metabolism and body temperature increase. Explain this finding briefly.

5.   The average male adult (160 lbs.) requires the consumption of food, which has the energy equivalent of about 2800 kcal of energy per day.

    a.   If this is derived from the hydrolysis of ATP under standard conditions, calculate the number of moles and the number of grams of ATP which would be synthesized each day.

    b.   It is found that there is about 50 g of ATP in the body. Considering this and the answer from part (a), suggest an explanation which is consistent with both findings.

6.   Indicate the cellular location of the following enzymes, molecules or processes. If the location is within the mitochondrion, specify whether it is in the matrix, inner membrane, inner membrane space or the outer membrane.

    a.   Pyruvate dehydrogenase complex

    b.   ATP synthetase

    c.   Citric acid cycle

    d.   Triose-phosphate isomerase

    e.   NADH

    f.   ATP

    g.   Malate

    h.   Pentose phosphate pathway

    i.   Cytochrome oxidase

    j.   Succinate dehydrogenase

7. The overall equation for the complete oxidation of glucose by molecular oxygen is:

$$C_6H_{12}O_6 \ + \ 6\,O_2 \ \ -----> \ \ 6\,CO_2 \ + \ 6\,H_2O$$

a. Write the two half-reactions for this redox process. These involve the oxidation of glucose to CO_2 and the reduction of O_2 to H_2O. Show the number of electrons involved in each half-reaction.

b. In the oxidation, indicate the electron acceptor molecule(s) which directly receive the electrons.

c. Indicate the molecules or enzymes to which the electrons are transferred to in the next phase of the process.

d. Which molecule or enzyme transfers the electrons directly to molecular oxygen?

8. The $\Delta G^{0'}$ for the complete oxidation of glucose is - 2823 kJ of energy per mole of glucose.

a. Calculate the percent of this energy that is efficiently converted to ATP in:
   i. Glycolysis
   ii. Pyruvate conversion to acetyl-CoA
   iii. Citric acid cycle
   iv. Electron transport and oxidative phosphorylation

b. Calculate the energy conversion efficiency in the complete oxidation of glucose in a living cell.

c. With the high negative value for $\Delta G^{0'}$ for this reaction, what can be predicted about the rate of the reaction?

9. List the functions carried out by ATP synthetase.

10. Indicate if the following statements are true or false. If the statement is false, change it to make it correct.

a. The standard potential for a redox reaction is directly related to the standard free energy for the reaction.

b. The greater the difference between the standard half-reaction potentials, the more spontaneous the reaction will be.

c. Water is the terminal electron acceptor in the electron transport chain.

d.   The larger the positive value of the standard reduction potential, $E^{0'}$, the stronger the oxidizing agent.

e.   Cytochrome a/a$_3$ $_{oxid}$ [Fe(III)] is a better oxidizing than cytochrome b$_{oxid}$.

f.   All four of the protein complexes which make up the mitochondrial respiratory electron transport chain contain [Fe-S] proteins.

g.   The reaction for the transfer of electrons from NADH to coenzyme Q has a $E^{0'}$ value of + 0.42 volts. Therefore, the standard half-reaction potential for the reduction of coenzyme Q is + 0.10 volts. (Refer to Table15.1 in the text).

ANSWERS TO EXERCISES

1.   a.   α-ketoglutarate
      b.   fumarate
      c.   fumarate
      d.   α-ketoglutarate

2.   a.

$$\Delta G^{0'} = -nFE^{0'} = -(2)(96,500 J/mol)[1.14\ V] = \underline{-220\ kJ/mol}$$

$$\Delta G^{0'} = -2.303\ logK_{eq}$$

$$\underline{K_{eq} = 3.8 \times 10^{38}}$$

b.   The oxidation of one mole of NADH in the respiratory chain results in the production or synthesis of three moles of ATP. Since the $\Delta G^{0'}$ for the hydrolysis of ATP is -30.5 kJ/mol, the synthesis of three moles of ATP requires the input of 91.5 kJ/mol of energy. The energy efficiency for the process is:

Efficiency = [91.5 kJ/mol]/[220 kJ/mol] x 100
Efficiency = 41.5 %

3. The three respiratory multienzyme complexes that serve as proton pumps are:

1. NADH-CoQ oxidoreductase.
2. $CoQH_2$-cytochrome c oxidoreductase.
3. Cytochrome oxidase.

(The F_0 functional subunit of ATP synthetase acts as a proton channel)

4. a. The addition of 2,4-dinitrophenol (DNP) uncouples electron transport from the phosphorylation of ADP to produce ATP. That is to say, if DNP is added to a mitochondrial suspension which has an oxidizable substrate (such as succinate), O_2 will be consumed, yet no ATP will be produced. If the same experiment is carried out without the DNP, both O_2 consumption and ATP synthesis is observed.

b. DNP can exist in the protonated or unprotonated form.

At intracellular pH, DNP is in the dissociated form because of the pK_a of the phenolic hydrogen. If the DNP is in the vicinity of the inner membrane, where the pH is lower ($[H^+]$ is greater), DNP becomes protonated and reduces the free H^+ concentration in the inner membrane space. The protonation converts DNP from a hydrophilic, anionic species to a neutral, hydrophobic species. The latter species is soluble in the inner membrane and passes through it. In this way, it passively takes the protons from the inner membrane space into the matrix, bypassing the F_0 channel in the ATP synthetase. As a result, ATP synthesis is uncoupled from the electron transport process. In the matrix where the pH is higher, the DNP dissociates the proton.

c. Since ATP levels will be decreased due to the uncoupling reaction, the regulation mechanisms in the cell will stimulate catabolic activity in order to promote the synthesis of ATP. However, this will not yield to ATP production because of the presence of the uncoupler. The body temperature will rise since the energy produced will be dissipated in the form of heat (and not used in ATP synthesis).

Apparently, for a short period in the 1940s, the administration of sublethal doses of DNP was actually prescribed to produce weight lose in overweight individuals.

5.   a.   If the 2800 kcals of energy is used to synthesize ATP under standard condition (7.3 kcal/mol), the number of moles of ATP produced would be:

[2800 kcal]/[7.3 kcal/ATP] = <u>384 moles ATP.</u>

The number of grams of grams of ATP would be:
[384 moles][505 g/mole] = <u>193,920 g. ATP</u>

This would correspond to over 427 pounds of ATP!

b.   The ATP produced is hydrolyzed very quickly to ADP and phosphate   and is then resynthesized thousands of times. The calculation shows that over 3878 times as much ATP is synthesized than is found in the body.
[193,920 g ATP hydrolyzed]/ [50 g ATP in all cells] = 3878.

6.   a.   Matrix of the mitochondrion
      b.   Inner membrane of the mitochondrion
      c.   Matrix of the mitochondrion, with succinate dehydrogenase being within the inner membrane
      d.   Cytoplasm
      e.   Throughout the cell
      f.   Throughout the cell
      g.   Cytoplasm and mitochondrion
      h.   Cytoplasm
      i.   Inner membrane of the mitochondrion
      j.   Inner membrane of the mitochondrion

7.   a.   The half-reactions can be written independently as:

Oxidation: $C_6H_{12}O_6 + 6 H_2O$ -----> $6 CO_2 + 24 H^+ + 24 e^-$

Reduction: $6 O_2 + 24 e^- + 24 H^+$ -----> $12 H_2O$

          $C_6H_{12}O_6 + 6 O_2$ -----> $6 CO_2 + 6 H_2O$

b.   The direct electron acceptors are NAD^+ and FAD, which are reduced to produce NADH and $FADH_2$, respectively.

c.   The electrons from the NADH are transferred to the first respiratory complex, the NADH-CoQ oxidoreductase, in the electron transport chain.

$FADH_2$ is produced in the citric acid cycle by succinate dehydrogenase, which resides in the inner membrane of the mitochondria. The electrons do not formally leave this complex and are transferred directly to coenzyme Q in the electron transport chain.

d.   The cytochrome oxidase transfers the electrons to O_2.

8.   a.
i.   **Glycolysis:**

$$C_6H_{12}O_6 + 2\,ADP + 2\,P_i + 2\,NAD^+ \longrightarrow$$
$$2\,CH_3COCO_2^- + 2\,ATP + 2\,NADH + 2\,H_2O + 2\,H^+$$

Glycolysis produces 2 ATPs.
% of energy = [2(30.5 kJ/mol)]/[2823 kJ/mol] x 100 =
                    2.1% of total energy

ii.   **Pyruvate Conversion to Acetyl-CoA:**

$$2\,CH_3COCO_2^- + 2\,NAD^+ + 2\,CoAS\text{-}H \longrightarrow$$
$$2\,Acetyl\text{-}CoA + 2\,NADH + 2\,CO_2$$

Pyruvate conversion to acetyl-CoA does not produce any ATPs directly.
There is no energy contribution directly (i.e., ATPs) from this reaction.

iii. Citric Acid Cycle:

$$2 \text{ Acetyl-CoA} + 4 \text{ H}_2\text{O} + 6 \text{ NAD}^+ + 2 \text{ FAD} + 2 \text{ ADP} + 2 \text{ P}_i \longrightarrow$$
$$+ 4 \text{ CO}_2 + 6 \text{ NADH} + 6 \text{ H}^+ + 2 \text{ FADH}_2 + 2 \text{ CoA-SH} + 2 \text{ GTP}$$

The citric acid cycle produces 2 GTPs directly (equivalent to 2 ATPs). % of energy = <u>2.1 % of total energy</u>. This is the same amount contributed by glycolysis.

iv. Electron Transport and Oxidative Phosphorylation:

$$10 \text{ NADH} + 10 \text{ H}^+ + 6 \text{ O}_2 + 2 \text{ FADH}_2 \longrightarrow$$
$$10 \text{ NAD}^+ + 2 \text{ FAD} + 12 \text{ H}_2\text{O}$$

The generation of ATP is derived from the transfer of the electrons from the energy-rich coenzymes into the electron transport chain and then to molecular oxygen. Each NADH oxidized generates 3 ATPs, while the oxidation of each $FADH_2$ results in the synthesis of 2 ATPs. Therefore, there is 34 ATPs produced.

% energy = (34)(30.5 kJ/mol)/[2823 kJ/ mol] x 100 =

<u>36.7 % of total energy</u>

b.   The total energy produced in the form of ATP is:

Glycolysis:	61 kJ/mol
Citric acid cycle:	61 kJ/mol
Electron transport and oxidative phosphorylation	1037 kJ/mol
	————————
	1159 kJ/mol

% energy efficiency = [1159 kJ/mol]/ [2823 kJ/mol] x 100 = <u>41 %</u>

c.   The free energy change is only an indication of the thermodynamic driving force for the reaction. There is no relationship between the $\Delta G^{0'}$ for a reaction and the rate of the reaction. Therefore, $\Delta G^{0'}$ values cannot be used to predict the rate of the reaction.

9.   ATP synthetase is the most complex assembly in the inner mitochondrial membrane. It contains many proteins and has two functional subunits, called F_0 and F_1. It carries out three functions. It catalyzes (1) the synthesis of ATP from ADP and phosphate, and (2) the

reverse reaction, the hydrolysis of ATP to yield ADP and phosphate. Recall that an enzyme catalyzes both the forward and reverse reactions. These reactions are carried out by the F_1 subunit. The complex also (3) provides a channel for the translocation of protons from the inner membrane space to the matrix. This is accomplished by the F_o subunit.

10.
    a.   True.

    b.   False.   The greater the difference and the more **positive** the potential, the more spontaneous the reaction.

    c.   False. O_2 is the terminal electron acceptor in the electron transport chain.

    d.   True.

    e.   True.

    f.   False.   Cytochrome oxidase does not contain [Fe-S] proteins.

    g.   True.

16

Lipid Metabolism

This chapter examines the metabolic processes associated with the catabolism and anabolism of a variety of lipid molecules. Triacylglycerols, being such highly reduced molecules, have the highest energy content of all the major nutrients. Fatty acid oxidation begins with the hydrolysis of the acylglycerol and the transport of the activated acyl group into the mitochondrion where the process of β-oxidation occurs. This cyclic pathway generates acetyl-CoA, which can be shuttled into the Krebs cycle, in addition to $FADH_2$ and NADH, which enter the electron transport chain and produce ATP by oxidative phosphorylation. Fatty acids with an odd number of carbon atoms or which have some degree of unsaturation are also oxidized by β-oxidation, but this requires additional reactions. In situations such as starvation or diabetes, an excess of acetyl-CoA is produced. The acetyl-CoA cannot enter the Krebs cycle and as a result, metabolites referred to as ketone bodies are formed. The biosynthesis of fatty acids is carried out in the cytosol by the successive addition of two-carbon units by the multienzyme complex, fatty acid synthetase. The anabolism of triacylglycerol, phosphoglycerol and sphingolipids is also briefly presented. The complex biosynthetic pathway for cholesterol is outlined, with a general overview presented for the conversion of cholesterol to bile salts and sex hormones. The role of serum cholesterol, low-density lipoprotein (LDL) particles and LDL receptors in cholesterol metabolism and in atherosclerosis is discussed.

CHAPTER OBJECTIVES

1.   Indicate the cellular locations for the initial hydrolysis of acylglycerol and phosphatidyl choline, β-oxidation of fatty acids and fatty acid biosynthesis.

2.   Outline the steps involved in the β-oxidation of fatty acids, starting with the hydrolysis of acylglycerol and including the transport mechanism that acyl groups utilize to enter the mitochondria.

3.   Calculate the number of ATP molecules produced in the complete oxidation of a saturated or unsaturated fatty acid.

4.   Consider the structures for the ketone bodies, the metabolic conditions in which they are produced and the reactions which describe their formation.

5.   Describe the role of acetyl-CoA, malonyl-CoA and the acetyl-CoA carboxylase complex, fatty acid synthetase and acyl carrier protein (ACP) in fatty acid biosynthesis.

6.   Summarize the important differences between the anabolic and catabolic pathways for fatty acids.

7.   Outline the general aspects of the anabolism of acylglycerols and sphingolipids.

8.   Name and characterize the major intermediates having C_2, C_6, C_5, C_{10}, C_{15}, and C_{30} units in the cholesterol biosynthetic pathway.

9.   Characterize the structures for bile salts and the male and female sex hormones which are derived from cholesterol.

10.   Describe the interrelationship between serum cholesterol levels, LDL and high-density lipoprotein (HDL) particles, LDL receptors and atherosclerosis.

SPOTLIGHT

Atherosclerosis:
Cholesterol and The LDL Connection

Cholesterol is essential in higher organisms for both growth and viability. It serves as a component in all plasma membranes and is a precursor for the synthesis of bile salts, steroid hormones and vitamin D. It is primarily synthesized in the liver and to a lesser extent in the intestine, with about 800 mg/day being produced in individuals on cholesterol-free diets. The major source of cholesterol in other cells is through the uptake of exogenous cholesterol in the form of serum LDL particles. The LDL particle (ca. 22 nm in diameter) provides the vehicle to transport insoluble cholesterol in the blood. When an animal cell requires cholesterol for membrane synthesis, it activates the synthesis of LDL receptor proteins and incorporates them in the cell membrane. The LDL particles actually contain esters of cholesterol, enveloped by a phospholipid layer which contains cholesterol and at least one molecule of apoprotein B-100. Circulating LDLs bind to the cell-surface transmembrane proteins, the LDL receptors, by interacting specifically with the apoprotein B-100. The receptors cluster in regions of the membrane called coated pits, and after complexing with LDLs, the regions invaginate and undergo <u>receptor mediated endocytosis</u>, as outlined in Figure 11.13 in the text. The particles are metabolized in the cell to produce cholesterol, fatty acids and amino acids. The cholesterol is then used primarily in membrane synthesis.

Failure of the LDL particles to be taken up by the cells results in abnormally high levels of serum cholesterol. Because of the inherent insolubility of cholesterol and especially the cholesterol esters which reside inside the LDL particle, after prolonged periods of high serum cholesterol levels, they deposit on the inside walls of blood vessels. The cholesterol produces a plaque and may ultimately block blood flow, resulting in a myocardial infarction, commonly known as a heart attack.

The failure of the LDLs to be taken into the cell can occur by a natural check-and-balance regulatory mechanism or, many times, as a result of mutations in the LDL receptors. In the former case, sufficient cholesterol within the cell suppresses endogenous cholesterol synthesis by inhibiting HMG-CoA reductase, the enzyme which catalyzes the committed step in cholesterol synthesis. Sufficient endogenous cholesterol also down regulates or suppresses the synthesis of LDL receptors, thereby restricting the uptake of additional cholesterol, beyond that needed by the cell. In this way, if there is a high level of cholesterol in the plasma, it remains there.

In addition, mutations in the LDL receptors can occur. These can result in any or all of the following ways:

1. Insufficient synthesis of receptors,
2. Receptors which are synthesized, but do not reach the plasma membrane,
3. Receptors that reach the membrane, but are defective and do not bind LDL particles,
4. Receptors that reach the membrane, bind LDL particles, but fail to cluster in the coated pits. Therefore, they do not undergo endocytosis.

The medical concern in all these situations, of course, is the same: high cholesterol levels in the blood produce a greater risk of heart disease.

There are at least two ways to help lower this risk. One is to increase the level of high density lipoproteins (HDLs) in the plasma. It appears that a diet rich in polyunsaturated fatty acids, such as found in fish and vegetable oils, can produce an increase in the HDL level. These particles, by some unknown mechanism, decrease the level of LDLs. One known function of the HDLs is to remove cholesterol from the peripheral tissues and return it _to_ the liver. In the liver, the primary fate of cholesterol is to make bile salts, which are then secreted into the intestines and subsequently excreted from the body. The increased level of HDLs therefore helps to eliminate cholesterol from the body.

An alternate way to reduce serum cholesterol levels is to administer the drug, mevinolin (also called lovastatin), which is a potent competitive inhibitor of HMG-CoA reductase. By inhibiting cholesterol synthesis in the cells in

156

this manner, the cell produces higher levels of LDL receptors and permits more LDL particles to enter the cells. This, therefore, reduces the levels of serum LDLs and the total cholesterol in the plasma.

EXERCISES

1. Acetyl-CoA is a molecule of central importance in cellular metabolism.
   a. Where is acetyl-CoA produced in the cell?
   b. Indicate the precursors of acetyl-CoA in the cell.

2. Match the characteristics in the right column with the lipid molecules in the left column.

a.	Sphingomyelin	1.	N-acylsphingosine
b.	Ganglioside	2.	Complete hydrolysis produces a fatty acid, choline, phosphoric acid and sphingosine
c.	Sphingosine	3.	Unsaturated 18 carbon chain containing an amine and two alcohol functional groups
d.	Ceramide	4.	Formed by attachment of an oligosaccharide, containing sialic acid, to the primary alcohol group of ceramide
e.	Cerebroside	5.	Glucose or other sugar is attached to the primary alcohol of ceramide

3. It is stated that all the carbon atoms in fatty acids are derived from the acetyl groups of acetyl-CoA (page 404 in the text). However, in Figure 16.10 in the text, it shows that the carboxylate group in malonyl-CoA, the key intermediate in fatty acid

biosynthesis, is derived from the bicarbonate anion. Explain how all the carbon atoms in fatty acids can therefore be derived from only the acetyl groups in acetyl-CoA.

4.   The biosynthesis of triacylglycerol begins with the synthesis of glycerol 3-phosphate (G3P) from either glycerol or dihydroxyacetone phosphate. What are the subsequent steps and the enzymes in the synthesis of triacylglycerol?

5.   In the metabolic pathway for cholesterol synthesis, the immediate precursor to mevalonate is β-hydroxy-β-methylglutaryl-CoA (HMG-CoA).
     a.   Write the equation for the formation of HMG-CoA. Include the name of the enzyme that catalyses this reaction.
     b.   The first committed step in cholesterol synthesis is the synthesis of mevalonate. Write the equation for this reaction, including the important enzyme which catalyzes the reaction.
     c.   Describe cholesterol in terms of the functional groups it exhibits, how many and what types of rings it has and indicate the number of asymmetric carbons or optically active carbon centers in the molecule.

6.   Consider a general acylglycerol in the cell. Outline the sequence of steps and the location of these events associated with the initial steps in fatty acid oxidation, up to the step at which the fatty acid enters in the β-oxidation pathway.

7.   In the β-oxidation of the acyl group, acetyl-CoA groups are formed in a step-wise manner. What is the chemical rational for the reactions which are involved in this process?

8.   a.   Name the three metabolic intermediates that are considered to be ketone bodies. Indicate which intermediates are actually ketones.
     b.   Indicate under what conditions ketone bodies are produced in the cells.

158

9. Compare the number of ATP molecules formed by the oxidation of one mole of palmitic acid under (a) normal conditions and also (b) severe starvation conditions. Consider, in this oversimplification, that in the extreme case, only an insignificant amount (none) of the acetyl-CoA enters the Krebs cycle. Therefore, only reduced coenzymes produced in the β-oxidation pathway enter the electron transport chain.

10. Indicate which of the terms in the right column is associated with the metabolic pathways in the left column.

a. Fatty acid oxidation _____

b. Fatty acid synthesis _____

1. Acyl-CoA

2. Malonyl-CoA

3. Occurs in cytoplasm

4. Uses NADPH

5. Involves β-ketoacyl-ACP reductase

6. In *E. coli,* pathway uses a multienzyme complex

7. Uses FAD

11. Indicate whether the statements below are true or false. If the statement is false, correct it.

a. In the fatty acid oxidation pathway, the enzyme, enol-CoA hydratase, requires a trans double bond arrangement between carbons 2 and 3.

b. The β-oxidation pathway occurs in the cytosol.

c. All of the carbons in cholesterol are derived from acetyl-CoA.

d. The oxidation of saturated fatty acids requires more reactions in their metabolic break down than the oxidation of unsaturated fatty acids.

e.   Before fatty acid synthesis can occur, acetyl-CoA must be transported out of the mitochondria and into the cytosol. This is accomplished by a transport mechanism in which oxaloacetate is transported across the membrane.

f.   ACP, which is part of the multienzyme complex called fatty acid synthetase, binds to acetyl or acyl groups by a thioether linkage.

g.   CTP is required for the biosynthesis of phosphatidylethanolamine in both bacteria and mammals.

ANSWERS TO EXERCISES

1.   a.   Acetyl-CoA is produced in the mitochondria of the cell.

b.   It can be formed from (1) decarboxylation of pyruvate, (2) β-oxidation of fatty acids and (3) from the catabolism of certain amino acids (Chapter 18).

2.   a.   2
      b.   4
      c.   3
      d.   1
      e.   5

3.   Malonyl-CoA is produced from acetyl-CoA and HCO_3^-, in a reaction catalyzed by acetyl-CoA carboxylase. Two of the three carbons in the malonyl group are derived from the acetyl group and one from the bicarbonate anion. The biosynthesis of fatty acids, however, involves the successive addition of only two carbon units, so only the carbons from the acetyl group are added to the growing chain. The carbon derived from the bicarbonate anion is eliminated in this reaction as a molecule of CO_2.

4. The reactions are the following:

$$\text{G3P} + \text{Acyl-CoA} \xrightarrow{\text{GPAT*}} \text{Lysophosphatidate} + \text{CoA-SH}$$

G3P = Glycerol 3-phosphate
*(GPAT = Glycerol phosphate acyl transferase)

$$\text{Lysophosphatidate} + \text{Acyl-CoA} \xrightarrow{\text{GPAT}} \text{Phosphatidate} + \text{CoA-SH}$$

$$\text{Phosphatidate} + \text{H}_2\text{O} \xrightarrow[\text{Phosphatase}]{\text{Phosphatidate}} \text{1,2-Diacylglycerol} + \text{P}_i$$

$$\text{1,2-Diacylglycerol} + \text{Acyl-CoA} \xrightarrow[\text{Acyl Transferase}]{\text{Diacylglycerol}} \text{Triacylglycerol} + \text{CoA-SH}$$

5.   a.

Acetoacetyl-CoA   Acetyl-CoA   β−Hydroxy-β-methylglutaryl-CoA

$$\underset{\text{CH}_3\text{-C-CH}_2\text{-C-S-CoA}}{\overset{\text{O} \quad\quad \text{O}}{\overset{\|\quad\quad\|}{}}} + \underset{\text{H}_3\text{C-C-S-CoA}}{\overset{\text{O}}{\overset{\|}{}}} + \text{H}_2\text{O} \xrightarrow{\text{E*}} {}^-\text{O}_2\text{C-CH}_2\text{-}\underset{\underset{\text{CH}_3}{|}}{\overset{\overset{\text{OH}}{|}}{\text{C}}}\text{-CH}_2\text{-}\overset{\overset{\text{O}}{\|}}{\text{C}}\text{-S-CoA}$$

$$+ \text{CoA-SH} + \text{H}^+$$

E* = Hydroxymethylglutaryl-CoA synthetase

b.

β−Hydroxy-β-methylglutaryl-CoA   Mevalonate

$$^-O_2C\text{-}CH_2\text{-}\underset{\underset{CH_3}{|}}{\overset{\overset{OH}{|}}{C}}\text{-}CH_2\text{-}\overset{\overset{O}{\|}}{C}\text{-}S\text{-}CoA \;+\; 2\,NADPH \xrightarrow{\;E^*\;} \;^-O_2C\text{-}CH_2\text{-}\underset{\underset{CH_3}{|}}{\overset{\overset{OH}{|}}{C}}\text{-}CH_2\text{-}CH_2OH$$

$$+\; 2\,NADP^+ \;+\; CoA\text{-}SH$$

E* = Hydroxymethylglutaryl-CoA reductase (HMG-CoA reductase)

c.   Cholesterol contains only two functional groups, an alcohol at C3 and an olefin linkage between carbons 5 and 6 in the 6-membered rings. There are 4 fused rings, one being a 5-membered, cyclopentane ring and three 6-membered rings, two being cyclohexane and the third being a cyclohexene ring.

There are eight asymmetric carbons in cholesterol located at positions 3, 5, 8, 9, 10, 13, 17 and 20. The numbering system for cholesterol is shown in the accompanying Figure.

Numbering System in Cholesterol

6.   In the cytosol, a lipase cleaves the acylglycerol to produce glycerol and fatty acids. The fatty acid reacts with an ATP to form an acyl-adenylate intermediate and pyrophosphate, with the latter being hydrolyzed to phosphates. The acyl-adenylate then is activated by formation of a thioester bond with CoA-SH. This latter reaction is catalyzed by acyl-CoA synthetase. The acyl-CoA is transported through the outer mitochondrial membrane, but cannot pass through the inner membrane into the matrix where the remaining reactions associated with oxidation are carried out. At this point, the acyl group is enzymatically transferred to carnitine by carnitine acyltransferase. The acyl carnitine crosses the inner membrane and then the acyl group is transferred back to CoA-SH. The activated acyl group is now ready to enter into the β-oxidation pathway in which two-carbon units are successively cleaved off the carboxyl end.

7.   Starting with a saturated acyl group with n carbons, the aim of the cycle is to produce acetyl units in a step-wise manner. These units will be in the form of acetyl-CoA which can then undergo further oxidation in the Krebs cycle. The step-wise process will involve converting the acyl group into a molecule which can be attacked by CoA-SH to produce an acetyl-CoA and an (n-2) acyl group. The process will continue until all acetyl-CoA units are produced.

To convert the hydrocarbon portion of the acyl group to a ketone, an organic chemist would reduce a (C-C) bond first to an olefin linkage, then hydrate it to form a secondary alcohol and finally oxidize this alcohol to a ketone (refer to summary of organic reactions in Chapter 4 of this problems book). This is the same rational and strategy taken in the cell.

8.   a.   The three metabolic intermediates that have historically been referred to as ketone bodies are:
Acetoacetate
Acetone
β-Hydroxybutyrate
The first two are ketones, while the third molecule is a hydroxy acid.

b.   Ketone bodies are formed during starvation conditions and in cases of diabetes. In the former case, there are no glucose or glycogen stores to generate energy via the Krebs cycle and oxidative phosphorylation. Large amounts of acetyl-CoA are produced from fatty acid oxidation, but the acetyl-CoA cannot enter the Krebs cycle because of a depletion of oxaloacetate. This cannot be generated because there is no pyruvate from glycolysis. The buildup of acetyl-CoA therefore results in the reaction of two molecules of acetyl-CoA to form acetoacetyl-CoA and ketone bodies.

Diabetes mellitus, in some ways, mimics starvation. Although there can be a plentiful supply of glucose in the blood, the cells are "metabolically starving" since the glucose cannot enter the cells to undergo conversion to pyruvate and then acetyl-CoA. The outcome in both starvation and diabetes is similar, with high levels of ketone bodies being produced in both cases.

9.   Palmitic acid contains 16 carbon atoms. It will require 7 cycles of the β-oxidation pathway to yield 8 moles of acetyl-CoA. This will produce 7 moles of $FADH_2$ and 7 moles of NADH.

The 8 moles of acetyl-CoA produced from 1 mole of palmitic acid will enter the Krebs cycle. For each mole of acetyl-CoA, one mole of $FADH_2$ and 3 moles of NADH are produced, in addition to one mole of GTP.

The NADH and $FADH_2$ enter the electron transport chain and produce ATP by oxidative phosphorylation.

Overall ATP produced:
1. β-oxidation: 7 $FADH_2$ (Goes to electron transport chain)
                        7 NADH   (Goes to electron transport chain)
                        8 acetyl-CoA   (Goes to Krebs cycle)

2. Krebs cycle: 8 $FADH_2$ (Goes to electron transport chain)
                        24 NADH   (Goes to electron transport chain)
                        8 GTP

3. Electron transport and oxidative phosphorylation:

Total FADH$_2$ 15 FADH$_2$ x 2 ATP =   30 ATP

Total NADH   31 NADH   x 3 ATP =   93 ATP

(From Krebs cycle)   8 GTP =   8 ATP equivalents

                                                    ———————
                                                    131 ATP

Deduct 2 ATP equivalents
due to the activation step.   - 2 ATP

                                                    ———————

                    Total   <u>129 ATP molecules</u>

A net total of 129 molecules of ATP are produced for each molecule of palmitic acid which is completely hydrolyzed.

In the case of severe starvation and considering the simplifications noted above, only the 7 NADH and the 7 FADH$_2$ produced in the β-oxidation of palmitic acid would yield ATPs. The acetyl-CoA molecules would go to produce ketone bodies. Within this approximation, the number of molecules of ATP produced is:

7 NADH x 3 ATPs   = 21 ATP

7 FADH$_2$ x 2 ATPs   = 14 ATP

                                    ———————
                                    35 ATP

Activation   - 2 ATP

                                    ———————

            Total   <u>33 ATP molecules</u>

[33 ATP/129 ATP] x 100 = <u>25.5 %</u>

Less than 26% of the normal energy would be produced under these conditions.

10.

a.   1, 6, 7

b.   1, 2, 3, 4, 5

11.
  a. True.
  b. False.   It occurs in the mitochondria
  c. True.
  d. False.   This is correct for unsaturated fatty acid synthesis.
  e. False.   Citrate is the molecule which is transported across
the membrane.
  f. False.   This involves a thioester linkage.
  g. True.

17

Photosynthesis

The sun is the ultimate source of all biological energy. Photosynthesis, which is the process that captures this radiant energy and converts it into chemical energy, can be regarded as two major processes. The first process involves a series of reactions in which solar energy is absorbed by chlorophyll molecules in the chloroplasts of green plants. This energy is then used to power endergonic reactions which produce carbohydrates and molecular O_2 from the simple precursors, H_2O and CO_2. Two structurally distinct photosystems, I and II, located in the thylakoid membrane of the chloroplast, are the light collection centers in which the excited chlorophyll molecules trigger a series of electron transfer reactions. These initial reactions are referred to as the "light reactions" and are used to produce O_2, ATP and NADPH. The reactions are strikingly similar to those observed previously in the mitochondria, where electron transport takes place by using membrane bound proton-pumping oxidoreductases. In this process, a proton gradient is established across the thylakoid membrane and this electrochemical force is used to drive the production of ATP. The second major process in photosynthesis involves the so-called "dark reactions" which use ATP and NADPH to reduce CO_2 to carbohydrates in the stroma of the chloroplasts. The fixation of CO_2 takes place via the metabolic loop called the Calvin cycle. In this process, ribulose 1,5-bisphosphate is the initial reactant which is regenerated in the process, while glucose is derived from glyceraldehyde 3-phosphate which leaves the cycle.

CHAPTER OBJECTIVES

1.   Write the simple equation which describes photosynthesis and a more descriptive equation which includes ATP and NADPH.

2.   Write the separate reactions for the light and the dark photosynthetic reactions.

3.   Describe a chloroplast, characterizing the stroma, thylakoid disks, grana and the thylakoid membrane structure.

4.   Indicate the locations where photosystems I and II are found and where the light reactions and the dark reactions take place in the chloroplasts.

5.   Characterize the structures and distinguish the roles of chlorophyll a, b and bacteriochlorophyll a, accessory pigments, photosynthetic units and reaction centers in photosynthesis.

6.   List the similarities and differences in the composition, photochemistry and functions for photosystems I and II.

7.   Make an ordered list of molecular species in the electron transport reactions involved in the production of NADPH and O_2 in photosystems I and II, respectively.

8.   Outline how ATP is produced in photosynthesis and, alternatively, the manner in which ATP production can also be accomplished by cyclic electron transport in photosystem I.

9.   Characterize the enzyme, ribulose1,5-bisphosphate carboxylase: oxygenase and specify its location and the reactions which it catalyzes.

10.   Indicate the role of transketolase and aldolase in the Calvin cycle.

11.   Describe how glucose is produced and ribulose1,5-bisphosphate is regenerated in the Calvin cycle.

12.   Outline the C_4 pathway for CO_2 fixation and its advantage in tropical plants.

EXERCISES

1. Select the molecules or functions (1-15) which are associated with items (a-e) in the listing below.

    a.   Photosystem I   _____

    b.   Photosystem II   _____

    c.   Calvin Cycle   _____

    d.   Chlorophyll   _____

    e.   Accessory pigments   _____

    f.   Reactions connecting   _____
        PS I and II

1. Chloroplasts	2. $\lambda < 700$ nm	3. Thylakoid membrane
4. ATP synthesis	5. O_2 synthesis	6. Transketolase
7. Phytol group	8. NADPH synthesis	9. Pheophytin
10. Stroma	11. Plastoquinone	12. Ferredoxin
13. Mn containing enzyme	14. 3-Phospho-glycerate	15. Xylulose 5-phosphate isomerase

2. Ribulose 1,5-bisphosphate carboxylase:oxygenase (RuBisCO) is the most abundant enzyme in nature and probably the most abundant protein also. It has been estimated that there are about 40 million **tons** of it in the world.

    a.   Where is RuBisCO found in the chloroplast?
    b.   How large is it and how many subunits make up this enzyme?
    c.   Indicate the reactions which RuBisCO catalyzes.

3.   Indicate whether the following statements are true or false. If the statement is false, correct it.

   a.   Tropical plants circumvent the Calvin cycle by synthesizing glucose by the C_4 pathway.
   b. Chl_{II}^+ is a strong oxidant in photosystem II and can reduce water. Chl_{II}^+ is reduced by the transfer of electrons from the H_2O.
   c.   In photosystem I, soluble ferredoxin is the acceptor molecule for the direct electron transfer from Chl_I^*.
   d.   Electrons pass from photosystem I to photosystem II by the electron transport chain.
   e.   The primary role of an accessory pigment, such as pheophytin, is to absorb light.
   f.   The energy of light at 680 nm is greater than that at 700 nm.
   g.   Photosystem I is involved with the production of NADPH, while photosystem II carries out the splitting of water to produce molecular oxygen.
   h.   Transketolases are enzymes which are involved in the transfer of C_2 units.
   i.   Photorespiration is known to be a very efficient process in its use of ATP and NADPH.
   j.   Cyclic electron transfer produces ATP under cellular conditions when the ratio of $NADPH/NADP^+$ is low.

4.   Although the Calvin cycle and the Krebs cycle are very different, they exhibit some common characteristics. Make a comparison of the two cycles.

5.   Both photosystems I and II (PS I and II) are involved in redox reactions. Indicate the species and the reactions in these photosystems which exhibit the following characteristics.
   a.
      i.   The strongest oxidizing agent in PS II: _____
      ii.   The species oxidized by this agent: _____
      iii.   Primary oxidation half-reaction carried out:

_____

b.
  i.   The strong reducing agent in PS I: _____
  ii.   The chain of species reduced by this agent:_____
  iii. Primary reduction half-reaction carried out:

  _____

c.   The products of the above reactions
      which take part in the dark reactions are: _____

d.   The overall equation for the light reaction is:

  _____

e.   Explain how ATP is generated as a result of this reaction.

f.   Indicate the fate of the products formed in the light reactions.

6.   Consider the light reactions in photosynthesis. Complete the following table or statements below.
  a.   How many photons are absorbed by PS I and by PS II for each electron flowing from H_2O to $NADP^+$?

Number of Photons

PS I   _____
PS II   _____
Total   _____

b.   To form one molecule of O_2:
  i.   _____ molecules of H_2O are oxidized.
  ii.   _____ electrons must flow from two molecules of H_2O to _____ two molecules of $NADP^+$ in order to produce _____ molecules of _____ .

c.   In the entire process of producing one molecule of O_2, a total of _____ photons must be absorbed, with _____ being absorbed by each photosystem.

7.   Summarize the processes occurring in PS I and PS II with respect to the overall light reaction.

8.   Consider the Calvin cycle:
      a.   How many complete turns of the cycle are required to produce one molecule of glucose?
      b.   Does the regeneration of ribulose 1,5-bisphosphate require more or less molecules of ATP than the synthesis of glucose?
      c.   After six complete turns of the Calvin cycle, how many molecules of glyceraldehyde 3-phosphate are produced and how many are used in the synthesis of glucose?

9.   Complete the following statements concerning the C_4 pathway for CO_2 fixation.
      a. CO_2 enters the plant leaf through the _____ cells, which are the outer most cells.
      b.   The CO_2 reacts with _____ to form _____.
      c.   Oxaloacetate is converted to malate by the enzyme

_____ .
      d.   _____ is the molecule which leaves the _____ cells to enter the _____ cells, where the reactions in the Calvin cycle take place.
      e.   The CO_2 which enters the Calvin cycle is derived from the decarboxylation of _____ , with _____ being the other product.

ANSWERS TO EXERCISES

1.   a.   1, 3, 8, 12
      b.   1, 2, 3, 5, 13
      c.   1, 6, 10, 14, 15
      d.   1, 2, 3, 7
      e.   1, 3
      f.   1, 3, 4, 9, 11

2.
    a.   RuBisCO is located on the stromal surface of the thylakoid membrane.

    b.   RuBisCO has a molecular weight of 560 kDa., with eight large subunits, of molecular weight 55 kDa. and eight smaller subunits, of molecular weight 15 kDa. Interestingly, the gene for the larger protein is encoded by a chloroplast gene, while the gene for the smaller subunit, is encoded by the DNA within the nucleus. This is also a case in which one of the subunits (55 kDa) exhibits a catalytic function, while the smaller (15 kDa) subunit is thought to be involved in a regulatory role.

    c.   RuBisCO is the abbreviation for <u>ribulose 1,5-bisphosphate carboxylase:oxygenase.</u> Therefore, it serves as both a carboxylase and an oxygenase.
    The carboxylase function is involved in the fixation of CO_2 which diffuses into the stroma. Ribulose 1,5-bisphosphate, a phosphorylated, five-carbon ketose (monosaccharide), reacts with CO_2 to form an unstable six-carbon intermediate, which splits apart to produce two molecules of 3-phosphoglycerate.
    RuBisCO is a fascinating and genuinely unique enzyme. The single active site in RuBisCO, which carries out the fixation of CO_2, is also the same active site which facilitates the oxidation of ribulose 1,5-bisphosphate to 3-phosphoglycerate and phosphoglycolate. This reaction initiates the process known as photorespiration. Note that this enzyme is classified as an <u>oxygenase</u> because it carries out an oxidation in which O_2 is not only involved, but becomes incorporated into the product, 3-phosphoglycolate. This reaction diverts ribulose 1,5-bisphosphate from the Calvin cycle under conditions of high O_2 levels and low CO_2 levels.

3.
    a. False.   The C_4 pathway leads to the Calvin cycle.
    b. False. Chl_{II}^+ is reduced by the transfer of electrons from water, while H_2O is oxidized to O_2 in the process.
    c. False. Chl_I^* transfers its excited electron to chlorophyll a.
    d. False.   The transfer of electrons is from PS II to PS I.
    e. False.   The accessory pigments are involved in both light-trapping reactions and electron transfer processes.
    f. True.   Recall that $E = h\upsilon = h(c/\lambda)$.
    g. True.

h. **True.** It transfers the two-carbon glycoaldehyde unit (see Figure 17.7 in the text).

i. **False.** It is very inefficient in the utilization of ATP and NADPH.

j. **False.** Cyclic electron transfer produces ATP when the ratio of $NADPH/NADP^+$ is high.

4.

Characteristic	Calvin Cycle	Krebs Cycle
1. Type of cycle	Reductive	Oxidative
2. ATP and $NAD(P)^+$	Uses ATP and NADPH	Generates ATP, NADH and $FADH_2$
3. General function	Carbohydrate synthesis	Central pathway in integration of metabolism; catabolism and anabolism of carbohydrates, proteins and lipids
4. Entering unit	CO_2 (C_1 unit)	Primarily acetyl (C_2 units) from acetyl-CoA
5. Regenerated molecule	Ribulose 1,5-bisphosphate	Oxaloacetate

5.

    a.   i. Chl_{II}^+

            ii. H_2O

            iii. $2\ H_2O \longrightarrow 4\ H^+ + 4\ e^- + O_2$

    b.   i. Chl_I^*

            ii.   chlorophyll a, bound ferredoxin, soluble ferredoxin, $NADP^+$.

            iii. $NADP^+ + 2\ e^- + H^+ \longrightarrow NADPH$

    c.   ATP and NADPH

    d. $2H_2O + 2\ NADP^+ \longrightarrow O_2 + 2\ NADPH + 2\ H^+$

e.   There are 2 hydrogen ions produced in the overall light reaction for every 2 molecules of water oxidized. In addition, a number of protons are produced in the reactions which connect PS II and PS I. Although the total number of protons is not firmly established, it is estimated that there are about two to three protons produced for each electron (i.e., 8-12 H^+ per molecule of O_2 formed). These protons are produced in the thylakoid space (note Figure 17.11 in the text) and the net result is a pH gradient across the thylakoid membrane. The pH in the thylakoid space is lower than in the stroma and the difference has been determined to be as great as 3.5 pH units. The protons can only pass through the membrane and into the stroma by going through the membrane-bound proton translocating ATP synthetase complex and thereby providing the thermodynamic driving force for the phosphorylation of ADP to produce ATP.

f. O_2 diffuses out of the chloroplasts. NADPH, along with the generated ATP, are utilized in the dark reactions for the synthesis of glucose.

6.   The half-reaction for the oxidation of water shows that for every two molecules of water oxidized, one molecule of O_2, four electrons and four protons are produced.

$$2\ H_2O \ \text{-------}>\ \ O_2 + 4\ H^+ + 4\ e^-$$

a.

<u>Number of Photons</u>

PS I	1
PS II	1
Total	2

b.   i.   2
       ii   4, reduce, 2, NADPH

c.   8, 4

7.   Upon absorption of light (λ < 700 nm) in PS I, an electron is excited and therefore expelled from the reaction center. This excited electron "flows down" a chain of electron carriers to $NADP^+$ and reduces it to NADPH. This process leaves an "electron hole" or a missing electron in PS I. This, in turn, is filled with an electron expelled from PS II by the capture of a photon of light with a wavelength < 680 nm. This electron is transferred from PS II to the electron transport chain and then to P700 in PS I. PS II now has an "electron hole" and this is filled by electrons arising from the oxidation of water. In the process, protons are produced to generate the proton gradient which drives the production of ATP. The molecular oxygen that is produced is released from the chloroplast.

8.   a.   Six turns of the Calvin cycle are required to produce one molecule of glucose.
      b.   Regeneration of ribulose 1,5-bisphosphate requires the hydrolysis of more molecules of ATP than does the synthesis of glucose.
      c.   Twelve molecules of glyceraldehyde 3-phosphate are generated. Only two molecules of glyceraldehyde 3-phosphate are used for glucose synthesis.

9.
      a.   mesophyll
      b.   phosphoenolpyruvate, oxaloacetate
      c.   malate dehydrogenase
      d.   Malate, mesophyll, bundle sheath
      e.   malate, pyruvate

Note the Figure below which briefly outlines the C_4 pathway.

Abbreviated Features of the C$_4$ Pathway in Plants

18

The Metabolism of Nitrogen

Nitrogen metabolism encompasses the biosynthesis and degradation of amino acids, porphyrins, purine and pyrimidine nucleotides and nitrogen containing hormones and coenzymes. The ultimate source of nitrogen in biological molecules is inorganic N_2, which must be "fixed" into a useable form such as NH_3. Important aspects of amino acid anabolism involve transamination and one-carbon transfer reactions which require pyridoxal phosphate and tetrahydrofolate coenzymes, respectively. The catabolism of amino acids involves the elimination of nitrogen by way of the urea cycle and the metabolism of the residual carbon skeleton by the citric acid cycle. Purine nucleotides are synthesized de novo by the step-wise building of the ring systems of the purine base on ribose 5-phosphate or alternatively, by the more energy efficient salvage pathway. The anabolism of pyrimidine nucleotides starts with the synthesis of the pyrimidine ring before it is attached to the ribose 5-phosphate. The pathway by which deoxyribonucleotides are synthesized from the ribonucleotides can be inhibited by molecules which are used in cancer chemotherapy.

CHAPTER OBJECTIVES

1.   Outline the general aspects for the metabolic journey of inorganic N_2 from nitrogen fixation to the incorporation of nitrogen into simple biomolecules such as amino acids.

2.   Name the major biological molecules which contain nitrogen.

3.   Characterize the nitrogenase enzyme complex and indicate the process it catalyzes.

4.   Describe the reactions which are involved in the process of nitrification.

5.   Indicate the carriers for one-carbon units, specify the groups which can be transferred and the molecules that are the one-carbon acceptors.

6.   Justify the statement that the citric acid cycle is amphibolic.

7.   Outline the major reactions, including the enzymes and cofactors involved in transamination reactions.

8.   State the basis for classifying an amino acid as either essential or non-essential.

9.   Outline the general aspects of the anabolism of porphyrins.

10.   Describe an inborn error in amino acid and nucleotide metabolism, the human diseases associated with them and the clinical consequences.

11.   Indicate the basis for classifying an amino acid as glucogenic or ketogenic.

12.   Outline the reactions involved in the urea cycle and indicate how this cycle is metabolically connected with the citric acid cycle.

13.   Indicate the molecular conversions involved in the pathways for purine and pyrimidine nucleotide biosynthesis.

14.   Outline the general features in the catabolism of the purine and pyrimidine nucleotides.

15.   Discuss the synthesis of deoxyribonucleotides from ribonucleotides and explain why specific inhibitors for these reactions can be utilized in cancer chemotherapy.

EXERCISES

1. The nitrogen fixation reaction for the conversion of inorganic N_2 to NH_3 has a standard free energy of -33 kJ/mol. The bond energy for the triple bond in N_2 is enormous, at 940 kJ/mol.

$$N_2 + 3 H_2 = 2 NH_3$$

The fixation of N_2 is not only vital to biological systems, but it is an important industrial process in the manufacture of ammonia for fertilizers. To make this reaction go to the right to a significant extent, the reaction is carried out **industrially** at very high temperature and pressure. Microorganisms, however, can not survive in such extreme conditions. The reaction is accomplished in multiple steps by the enzyme, nitrogenase, and requires the input of about 12 molecules of ATP.

a. Write 3 distinct reactions for the step-wise reduction of N_2, assuming that in each step two reducing equivalents (one equivalent being either a H or a H^+ and an e^-) are added.

b. With a ΔG^0 of -33 kJ/mol, which indicates a spontaneous reaction, why are such drastic conditions needed industrially and such an elaborate enzyme complex necessary to produce NH_3 in nitrogen-fixing bacteria?

2. The following molecules are involved in the conversion of serine to glycine: pyridoxal phosphate, serine hydroxymethylase and tetrahydrofolate.

a. Indicate the role of each of these molecules in the conversion process.

b. What type of bond is formed between the amino acid and the pyridoxal phosphate?

3. The citric acid cycle is said to be amphibolic.

a. What does this expression mean?

b. Indicate the four intermediates in this cycle that serve as entry points for the catabolism of amino acids.

c.   Indicate the two intermediates in the citric acid cycle which serve as intermediate precursors for the anabolism of amino acids.

4.   Name the three important one-carbon carriers encountered in metabolic processes.

5.   a.   Indicate why an amino acid is designated as glucogenic, ketogenic or both glucogenic and ketogenic?
       b.   Explain why organisms that have a glyoxylate cycle do not have ketogenic amino acids.

6.   a.   There are two "molecular-links" between the urea cycle and the citric acid cycle. Name these two molecules and indicate the nature of the linkage.
       b.   It is stated that the two cycles are linked by the formation and breakdown of a single intermediate in the urea cycle. What is this metabolic intermediate? Explain this briefly in light of your answer in (a).
       c.   How many molecules of ATP are involved in the synthesis of urea and how many high energy bonds are hydrolyzed?
       d.   Urea has two nitrogen atoms. What are the molecular sources of these nitrogens which are eliminated in the form of urea?

7.   a.   What are the substrates for the salvage reactions in nucleotide metabolism?
       b.   Indicate the reactions and the enzymes used in the salvage synthesis of purine nucleotides.

8.   Aspartate transcarbamoylase (ATCase) is one of the most extensively studied regulatory enzymes.
       a.   Is this a simple or a multisubunit enzyme?
       b.   Does it follow Michaelis-Menten kinetics?
       c.   Write the equation for the reaction that it catalyzes?
       d.   What does it mean for a reaction to be the "committed " step of a metabolic pathway?
       e.   What are the allosteric effectors for aspartate transcarbamoylase?

181

9.   Ribonucleotides are synthesized initially and then converted to deoxyribonucleotides.
a.   Write the reaction associated with this conversion. Indicate the enzyme and the proteins associated with this reaction.
b.   What type of reaction is this?
c.   What are the common abbreviations for the nucleoside diphosphates produced in this reaction?
d.   How are thymine nucleotides produced from uracil nucleotides? Write the equation for this reaction, including the enzyme and any cofactors.

10.   Indicate whether the statement below is true or false. If the statement is false, correct it.

a.   Nitrate reductase and nitrite reductase are essential enzymes in the nitrification process.
b.   When an excess of amino acids is taken in, beyond that needed for the synthesis of proteins, the amino acids are stored and then used as needed.
c. α-Ketoglutarate is the major acceptor for amino groups from the other amino acids.
d.   Pyridoxal phosphate, which serves as a coenzyme in transamination reactions, is bound to the enzyme by a Schiff base linkage.
e.   The carbon unit involved in the one-carbon transfers with tetrahydrofolate cofactors is bonded to either the N^5 or the N^{10} atoms or both nitrogen atoms.
f.   In purine nucleotide biosynthesis, the purine ring system is assembled on the ribose 5-phosphate, while in pyrimidine biosynthesis, the pyrimidine ring is synthesized before being attached to the ribose 5-phosphate.
g.   The salvage pathway for the biosynthesis of purine nucleotides is complex and requires a great deal of energy. As a result, it is used in the cell as only a last resort for purine nucleotide synthesis.
h.   Lesch-Nyhan syndrome is associated with a deficiency of the enzyme, hypoxanthine-guanine phosphoribosyltransferase (HPRT).
i.   Inhibitors of folate reductase, such as fluorouracil, are widely used in cancer chemotherapy.
j.   Ribonucleotides are precusors for deoxyribonucleotides.

ANSWERS TO EXERCISES

1. a. The distinct steps in this reaction are:
    1. $N_2 + 2 H^+ + 2 e^-$ --->   H-N=N-H
    2. $H-N=N-H + 2 H^+ + 2 e^-$ ---> H_2N-NH_2
    3. $H_2N-NH_2 + 2 H^+ + 2 e^-$ ---> $2 NH_3$

    b. The ΔG^0 for a reaction represents the thermodynamic driving force for the reaction and is an indication of whether the reaction goes to the right to generate products. The ΔG^0 value, however, does not indicate the rate at which this reaction will take place. Although this reaction is spontaneous and will go to the right, there are effectively no products formed under standard conditions. The reaction has an extremely high energy of activation which must be overcome for ammonia to form. This energy barrier can be overcome by increasing the temperature and pressure, in line with Le Chatelier's principle. Alternatively, the reaction can be accomplished enzymatically, with the enzyme providing an alternate route for the reaction, in which the activation energy is significantly lowered.

2. a. Serine hydroxymethylase is the enzyme responsible for the catalytic conversion of serine to glycine. Pyridoxal phosphate is the coenzyme which is required for transamination reactions. (It also takes part in amino acid decarboxylations, racemizations and a number of modifications of the amino acid side group). The tetrahydrofolate is the coenzyme which is involved in the transfer of the single carbon unit.
    b. A Schiff base linkage is formed between the amino acid and the pyridoxal phosphate.

3.   a.   An amphibolic cycle is one involved in both catabolism and anabolism.

        b.   α-Ketoglutarate, succinyl-CoA, fumarate and oxaloacetate serve as entry points into the Krebs cycle for the metabolic breakdown of some amino acids.

        c.   α-Ketoglutarate and oxaloacetate serve as intermediate precursors for the biosynthesis of some amino acids.

4.   The three one-carbon carriers are:

        biotin (CO_2);

        tetrahydrofolate (methyl, methylene, methenyl, formimino or formyl groups);

        S-adenosylmethionine (CH_3 groups).

5.   a.   After the removal of the nitrogen from the amino acids, the carbon skeletons of the normal amino acids may be degraded to one or more of the following metabolic intermediates:

     1.   acetoacetyl-CoA
     2.   acetyl-CoA
     3.   pyruvate
     4.   α-ketoglutarate
     5.   succinyl-CoA
     6.   fumarate
     7.   oxaloacetate

The carbon skeletons of the **glucogenic** amino acids are degraded to the intermediates, 3 through 7. All of these can be used as precursors for glucose.

The carbon skeletons for the **ketogenic** amino acids are converted to either acetoacetyl-CoA or acetyl-CoA and can then be converted to ketone bodies. Since animals lack a metabolic pathway for the **NET** conversion of acetoacetate or acetyl-CoA to glucogenic precursors, no **NET** synthesis of glucose or carbohydrate is possible.

        b.   Plants and some microorganisms have a glyoxylate cycle. This cycle makes the **NET** synthesis of glucose synthesis possible for all the amino acids. In the glyoxylate cycle, there is a net synthesis of oxaloacetate from two molecules of acetyl-CoA. The oxaloacetate formed can be used in gluconeogenesis. However, in the Krebs cycle, the conversion of acetyl-CoA to oxaloacetate is accompanied by the elimination of two molecules of CO_2. As a result of this elimination. the **NET** synthesis of carbohydrate from acetyl-CoA (a C_2 group) is impossible.

The following Figure shows the seven common metabolic intermediates and the amino acids (the carbon skeletons) which are degraded to each intermediate. Although there is general agreement regarding the degradation pathway for the amino acids, there is not universal agreement with the assignments in the diagram below.

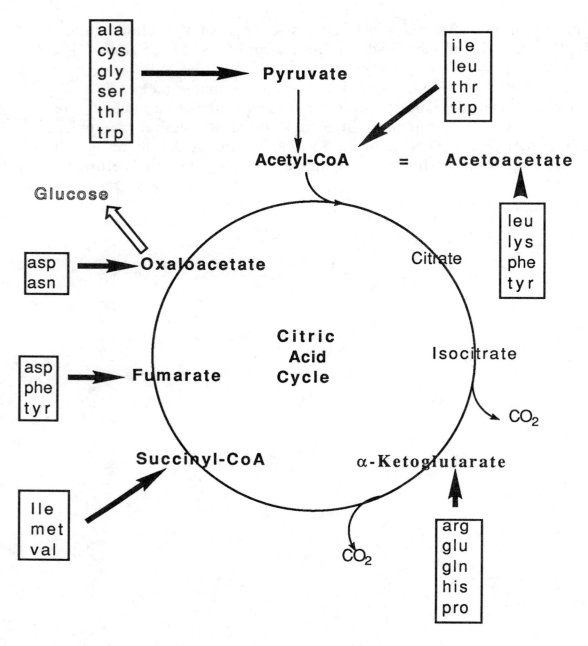

Amino acids are degraded to 7 metabolic intermediates

6. a.   The two molecules which link the urea and citric acid cycle are fumarate and aspartate. Fumarate is a product which exits the urea cycle in the reaction which splits argininosuccinate. The other product of this reaction is arginine, the immediate precursor of urea (and ornithine). Fumarate can then shuttle into the citric acid cycle, where it is one of the intermediates.

Aspartate, which contributes the second nitrogen in the formation of urea, is produced by the transamination of oxaloacetate by glutamate. The aspartate enters the urea cycle by reaction with citruline to form argininosuccinate.

b.   The urea cycle and the citric acid cycle are therefore linked by the synthesis and breakdown of argininosuccinate in the urea cycle.

c.   There are three molecules of ATP utilized in the production of urea. Two of the ATPs are hydrolyzed to ADP and P_i, while the third ATP is hydrolyzed to AMP and PP_i (pyrophosphate). The PP_i is further hydrolyzed to 2 P_i (phosphate). There are therefore four high energy bonds hydrolyzed in the process.

d.   One nitrogen comes from NH_4^+, while the second nitrogen is derived from aspartate.

7.   a.   The substrates are adenine, hypoxanthine and guanine. Salvage synthesis for the pyrimidines is generally less significant.

b.   There are three reactions and two enzymes involved in the salvage synthesis of purine nucleotides.

a. $$\text{Adenine} + \text{PRPP} \xrightarrow{E_1} \text{AMP} + PP_i$$

$$E_1 = \text{adenine phosphoribosyltransferase}$$
$$\text{PPRP} = \text{phosphoribosylpyrophosphate}$$

b. $$\text{Hypoxanthine} + \text{PRPP} \xrightarrow{E_2} \text{IMP} + PP_i$$
$$\text{Guanine} + \text{PRPP} \xrightarrow{E_2} \text{GMP} + PP_i$$

$$E_2 = \text{hypoxanthine-guanine phosphoribosyltransferase}$$

8.   a.   ATCase is a multisubunit enzyme, as are all regulatory enzymes.

b.   Allosteric enzymes do not obey Michaelis-Menten kinetics.

c.

$$\text{Aspartate} \qquad \text{Carbamoyl phosphate}$$

$$^-OOC\text{-}CH_2\text{-}\overset{\overset{\displaystyle H}{|}}{\underset{\underset{\displaystyle NH_3^+}{|}}{C}}\text{-}COO^- \quad + \quad H_2N\text{-}\overset{\overset{\displaystyle O}{\|}}{C}\text{-}OPO_3^{\,-2}$$

ATCase $\longrightarrow$ PO_4^{-3}

Carbamoyl aspartate

d.   Molecules synthesized in steps before the committed step in a metabolic pathway may have a number of metabolic fates. The products of a committed step are restricted to a single, specific purpose. The products of the committed step in pyrimidine synthesis are used only to produce pyrimidines.

e.   CTP is an allosteric inhibitor, while ATP is an allosteric activator for ATCase.

9.   a.   **Ribonucleotide diphosphate** + NADPH + H$^+$ ------>

Deoxyribonucleotide diphosphate + NADP$^+$ + H$_2$O

Ribonucleotide reductase is the enzyme, with thioredoxin and thioredoxin reductase playing an essential role in the shuttling of the electrons from NADPH to the dNDP molecule.

188

    b.   This is a redox reaction in which NDP becomes reduced to dNDP, as NADPH becomes oxidized to NADP$^+$.

    c.   dADP, dGDP, dCDP and dUDP.

    d.   dTMP is synthesized from dUMP by the enzyme, thymidylate synthetase, with N^5, N^{10}-methylenetetrahydrofolate serving as the methyl donor.

Biosynthesis of dTMP

dUMP N^5, N^{10}-methylene-FH$_4$

Thymidylate synthetase

dTMP   Dihydrofolate

10.   a.   True

     b.   False.   Amino acids are not stored. They are catabolized if they are not used for protein synthesis.

     c.   True.

     d.   False.   Although pyridoxal phosphate is the coenzyme in the transamination reactions, the Schiff base linkage is to the amino acid and not the enzyme.

     e.   True.

     f.   True.

     g.   False.   It involves only one reaction and requires less energy than the de novo synthesis of purine nucleotides.

     h.   True.

     i.   False.   Fluorouracil, although used in cancer chemotherapy, is an inhibitor for thymidylate synthetase.

     j.   True.

19

Summary of Metabolism

An enormous number of diverse, yet interconnected reactions are occurring at any one time in the life of every cell. Because of the interdependence of so many of these reactions, the metabolic pathways must be regulated. In addition, an ongoing intercellular communication is essential in multicellular organisms to coordinate the activities of the individual cells and tissues for homeostasis and the optimum functioning of the organism. This regulation is carried out at many levels.Within the cell, metabolic pathways are regulated by allosteric enzymes within feedback loops and many processes are limited to only certain organelles. Therefore, many metabolic intermediates must be transported from one compartment to another. Furthermore, intercellular communications are carried out by hormones, which bind to receptors either on or within the target cells. A variety of mechanisms, some including secondary messengers, are then engaged to control the desired metabolic changes within the cell. Finally, the character of muscle cells is presented and the role of ATP in the mechanism of muscle contraction is outlined.

CHAPTER OBJECTIVES

1.   Discuss the features of the citric acid cycle which emphasize its central role in cellular metabolism.

2.   Make a list of the major metabolic pathways and indicate the cellular location where each takes place.

3.   Catalog nutrients as macronutrients, micronutrients and minerals and indicate their role in providing proper nutrition.

4.   Indicate the key reactions and metabolic intermediates in the anabolism of carbohydrates.

5.   Specify the role of malate dehydrogenase, malate enzyme and malate in the transport of oxaloacetate across the mitochondrial membrane for carbohydrate and lipid anabolism.

6.   Trace the steps associated with hormone action from the initial signal from the central nervous system to the alteration of intracellular metabolism in the target cell.

7.   Characterize the known secondary messengers and indicate their role in hormone action.

8.   Define the gross structural characteristics of a myofibril.

9.   Outline the mechanism of muscle contraction.

EXERCISES

1.   Review the major metabolic pathways discussed in previous chapters. Indicate the pathways which are (a) linear or (b) cyclic in character. Linear pathways involve a series of enzymatically catalyzed reactions in which the product of one reaction is the substrate for the following enzyme. A cyclic pathway is similar, but requires that one of the metabolites be regenerated at the completion of the cycle.

192

② Suggest a reason for the possible toxicity associated with the ingesting of high levels of fat-soluble vitamins.

③ Oxaloacetate is a metabolite of central importance in the life of the cell. It takes part in the citric acid cycle and is a key intermediate in gluconeogenesis and amino acid biosynthesis. The level of oxaloacetate in the cell must be regulated so that it is at sufficient levels to accommodate acetyl-CoA that enters the citric acid cycle. In mammals, oxaloacetate can be synthesized in the mitochondria by the enzymatic carboxylation of pyruvate by pyruvate carboxylase (PC).

$$\text{pyruvate} + CO_2 + ATP + H_2O \xrightarrow{\text{PC}} \text{oxaloacetate} + ADP + P_i + 2 H^+$$

The activity of PC is regulated by the level of acetyl-CoA in the mitochondria. Suggest a general mechanism for this regulation.

4. Both hormones and neurotransmitters take part in intercellular communications. What property or properties distinguish a hormone from a neurotransmitter?

5. List the general functions of hormones and give an example of a hormone which fits into each category.

6. A human gene, referred to as the **ras** gene, exists in normal cells. However, specific mutations (changes in one or more of the bases in the DNA) can produce severe consequences to the organism. These mutations can cause the originally normal cell to undergo a transformation into a rapidly dividing tumor cell. In fact, it has been established that a number of mutated ras genes are associated with the occurrence of human cancers. Genes that have this characteristic are called cellular "**oncogenes**". The normal ras gene codes for a 21 kDa. protein, in which there are regions homologous (very similar in sequence) to the sequence of the α-subunit of the G protein. Like the G protein, the normal protein product of the ras gene is a guanine nucleotide binding protein and hydrolyzes GTP (exhibits a GTPase activity). However, although the protein product of the ras oncogene binds GTP, it has little or no GTPase activity.

193

a.   Suggest where you might expect to find the protein product of the ras oncogene in the cell.

b.   Suggest a possible mechanism of action for this protein which might stimulate cell growth.

7.   A group of natural products (naturally occurring organic compounds) are classified as phorbol esters. These natural products can stimulate the formation of tumors in animals when they are applied simultaneously with a carcinogen (a compound which produces cancer in animals). It has been established that phorbol esters produce this effect by activating protein kinase C.

a.   What are the names of the compounds with the abbreviations PIP_2, IP_3 and DAG?

b.   Which are considered to be second messengers?

c.   From an examination of the structures of the phorbol ester with IP_3 and DAG shown below, suggest a mechanism for the action of phorbol esters.

Phorbol   ester

Diacylglycerol

Inositol   1,4,5-triphosphate

$P^* = PO_3^{-2}$

8. Consider the composition and arrangement of these components in a muscle fiber (i.e., a muscle cell). Match the items in the right column with the corresponding terms in the left column.

a. Thin filaments | 1. Includes the region of thick filaments and region of overlapping thin and thick filaments.

b. Thick filaments | 2. Repeating units in myofibrils

c. H zone | 3. Myosin protein

d. Myofibrils | 4. Zones which contain only thick filaments.

e. An A band | 5. Actin, troponin and tropomyosin

f. Sarcomere | 6. Individual muscle fibers

9. The following Figure shows a schematic drawing of a skeletal myofibril. Using the list below, label the structures and the regions indicated.

Myofibril   A band   I band

Z line   H zone   Thin filament

Sarcomere   M line   Thick filament

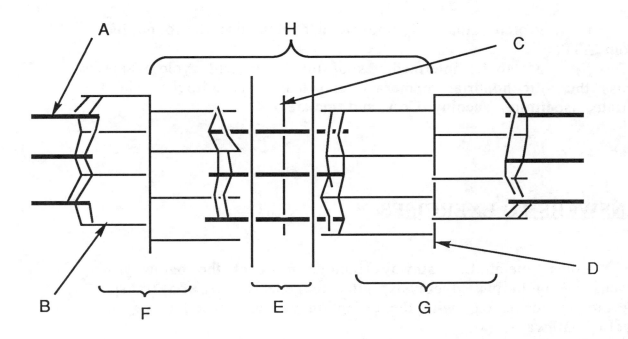

10. Indicate whether the following statements are true or false. Correct the false statements.

a. Oxaloacetate produced in the mitochondria can readily cross the membrane and enter the cytosol.

b. The B vitamins are essential nutrients since they cannot be synthesized in humans and are the precursors for metabolically important coenzymes.

c. The Food and Nutrition Board in the United States suggests a recommended daily allowance of nutrients for the average man or woman. For all the nutrients, the recommended amounts are greater for men than for women.

d. A reaction (such as the carboxylation of pyruvate to form oxaloacetate) which maintains an adequate level of metabolic intermediates is called an anaplerotic reaction.

e. All hormones exert their effect by an interaction with a plasma membrane receptor protein on the outside of the cell. The hormones do not enter the cell to produce their metabolic effect.

f. Hormones are a diverse group of molecules which include proteins, polypeptides, derivatives of amino acids and steroids.

g. Electron microscopy permits the observation of the light and dark bands in the myofibrils of muscle.

h. Actin has ATPase activity.

i.   Protein kinase C binds to adenylate cyclase to produce cAMP from ATP.

   j.   Metabolic intermediates of the citric acid cycle which can cross the mitochondrial membrane and leave the mitochondria are citrate, isocitrate, succinyl-CoA and malate.

ANSWERS TO EXERCISES

1.   Linear metabolic pathways include most of the pathways discussed, including glycolysis, gluconeogenesis, electron transport, steroid synthesis, etc, with the exception of those listed below as cyclic pathways.

   Cyclic pathways include the citric acid cycle, urea cycle and the Calvin cycle. It would also include the β-oxidation pathway for fatty acids (this may be regarded as spiral in character in that the acyl chain is progressively shortened by C_2 units).

2.   Fat soluble vitamins accumulate in the adipose tissue and because of their inherent solubility, can remain there for long periods of time. They are not as readily excreted as are the water-soluble vitamins. Therefore, high levels can accumulate in the fat to produce deleterious effects.

3.   It has been established that acetyl-CoA is a powerful allosteric effector of pyruvate carboxylase, in which the acetyl-CoA interaction with PC stimulates enzyme activity. In fact, PC is virtually inactive when acetyl-CoA is not bound to it. At low acetyl-CoA levels, the acetyl-CoA enters the TCA cycle and combines with oxaloacetate to form citrate. It does not bind to PC. However, at high acetyl-CoA levels, it would both enter the citric acid cycle and also interact with PC. This interaction stimulates the synthesis of oxaloacetate at sufficient levels to react with the intermediates derived from the acetyl-CoA entering the cycle. In addition, a fraction of the oxaloacetate can be diverted out of the cycle to produce phosphoenolpyruvate and subsequently glucose via gluconeogenesis.

4.   Both hormones and neurotransmitters are synthesized in specific cells, secreted and bind to receptors to produce or alter an activity. In fact, a number of molecules epinephrine (adrenaline) and norepinephrine have been characterized as both hormones and neurotransmitters. Therefore, the distinction cannot be assigned simply on the chemical nature of the molecule. The definition must rely on the function it carries out (i.e., its physiological nature). A major distinction between hormones and neurotransmitters depends on the distance over which it acts. Neurotransmitters act over the very short distance across a synapse (2×10^{-6} cm), while a hormone acts over long distances (many centimeters). The hormone is secreted from the endocrine gland and travels through the blood stream to interact with a distant target cell.

5.

Function	**Example**
1. Homeostasis	Insulin and glucagon (in controlling glucose levels)
2. Mediate a response to external stimuli	Epinephrine and norepinephrine
3. Growth and development	Female or male sex hormones

6.   a.   The ras protein would be expected to be a component of the plasma membrane similar to that of the G proteins. This is, in fact, where it is actually found in the cell.
        b.   It most likely exhibits the same function as that of the G proteins. That is, it is involved in signal transduction, which results in the production of cAMP as a result of hormone binding to the plasma membrane receptor. Recall that the G protein is in the inactive form when GDP is bound to the α-subunit and becomes activated when GTP binds it. Upon the hydrolysis of GTP to GDP, the protein again is cycled back to the inactive form. However, since the oncogenic ras protein does not have a GTPase activity, this protein is persistently in the activated form and therefore raises the level of cellular metabolism. This continuously increased activity would disrupt the regulation of normal growth and possibly produce unregulated cell division. Although this theory remains to be proven, it is a major

avenue of cancer research which is currently being pursued by many biomedical researchers in the world.

7.   a.

PIP_2;	Phosphatidylinositol 4,5-bisphosphate
IP_3;	Inositol 1,4,5-triphosphate
DAG;	Diacylglycerol (This must be a **1,2**-diacylglycerol.)

b.   The second messengers are IP_3 and DAG.

c.   The structure of DAG and the upper segment of the phorbol ester are very similar. This suggests that these molecules may exhibit comparable solubilities in the lipid bilayer, interact with protein kinase C by similar interactions and consequently act by similar mechanisms in activating protein kinase C.

8.   a. 5   b. 3   c. 4

d. 6   e. 1   f. 2

9.   A.   Thick filament (myosin)   B.   Thin filament (actin)

C.   M line   D.   Z line

E.   H zone   F and G.   Both are I bands

H.   Sarcomere

10.
a.   False.   Oxaloacetate must be transported by the the malate transport mechanism.
b.   True.
c.   False.   (Refer to Table 19.1 in the text). It is true for all nutrients except Fe, for which a higher level is recommended for women.
d.   True.
e.   False.   Not all hormones act in this manner. Steroid hormones enter the cell and bind to intracellular receptors within the cell.
f.   True.

g. True.

h. False. Myosin is the ATPase essential for muscle contraction.

i. False. It phosphorylates target proteins and enzymes, including those proteins that regulate the flow of Ca^{+2} ions into and out of the cell.

j. True.

20

The Structure of Nucleic Acids

Deoxyribonucleic acid (DNA) is a vital and multifunctional biomacromolecule. It is the repository for the genetic information in all cellular life forms. In addition, it provides the molecular vehicle for the expression of this genetic information during the life of the cell and for the transmission of hereditary characteristics from one generation to the next. The composition and structures (A, B and Z forms of DNA) of this polynucleotide are presented and characterized to provide the basis for understanding its essential role in the processes of replication, transcription and recombination. These important cellular transactions are presented in more detail in the following chapter. The three forms of cellular ribonucleic acid (RNA) are described and their roles in the translation process are outlined. Cellular nucleases that act on DNA and RNA substrates are described, with the character of and the pivotal role that restriction endonucleases play in the sequencing of DNA and in recombinant DNA technology highlighted.

CHAPTER OBJECTIVES

1.   Draw the nucleotides, nucleosides and the purine and pyrimidine bases found in DNA and RNA.
2.   Write out the numbering scheme for the purine and pyrimidine bases and the sugar unit and draw the phosphodiester backbone that links the nucleotides in nucleic acids.
3.   Make a list of the major structural features of DNA and RNA.
4.   Describe the hydrogen bonding interactions in the (GC) and (AT) complementary base pairs.
5.   Characterize supercoiled DNA and describe the role of topoisomerases in changing the tertiary structure of circular DNAs.
6.   Identify the different types of RNA molecules and characterize each type in terms of their size, abundance and function in the cell.
7.   Outline the procedures that are used to determine the primary structure of RNA and DNA.
8.   Describe the binding and cutting characteristics of restriction endonucleases and indicate their role in DNA sequencing and recombinant DNA technology.
9.   Summarize the relationship between the denaturation of DNA, the melting temperature (T_m) value for the DNA and the observed hyperchromicity.

SPOTLIGHT

DNA in Court:
"Molecular Fingerprint" Evidence

A fight erupts in an apartment, a shot is fired, the next-door neighbor dials 911, and an hour later, the police file a homicide report. A suspect is arraigned and pleads innocent. There are no witnesses and only a precious few pieces of evidence appear useful to the prosecution. A strand of hair, the same color as that of the suspect, was found under the fingernail of the victim. A modern forensic scientist takes this microgram specimen, analyzes the DNA in it and determines if it is identical to the DNA isolated from the suspect. If it is, this will provide virtually indisputable evidence that the suspect is the murderer.

The basis for this "molecular fingerprinting" lies in the finding that there are small segments of DNA (a few hundred base pairs) which occur repeatedly, from 4 to ca. 500 times, in humans. These sequences [called "minisatellite DNA" (MS DNA)] are similar in all persons, but are unique for each individual, due to different mutations (changed bases). The DNA can be digested with a restriction enzyme to produce a number of DNA fragments of different sizes. The number and the sizes of these DNA fragments will be dependent on the number of copies of MS DNA and the specific mutations in the DNA of each individual. Consider the DNAs in Figure 1 from three different individuals.

<u>Figure 1</u> <u>DNA Samples From Three Individuals</u>

Number of Fragments Containing MS DNA

1   3

2   2

3   3

DNA Polymorphism in "Minisatellite DNA"

Key: ▨ , MS DNA; ||||||| , DNA

Notice that all three DNAs contain multiple copies of the MS DNA. However, sample 2 contains a mutation which results in the deletion of the 5'-end of the second MS DNA. Sample 3 has multiple mutations which have resulted in a large deletion of DNA between the MS DNA repeats. A restriction enzyme, such as Eco RI, is used to digest these DNA samples. The <u>recognition sites occurs at the 5'-end of each intact MS DNA segment</u> and at the 3'-end of the DNA shown. After digestion, the DNA fragments are separated by gel electrophoresis (Figure 2). Because of the inherent uniqueness in the sequence of each DNA, a distinct

204

pattern of bands will be observed for each DNA sample. Although millions of bands will be produced in the digestion of human DNA, the interest is on only those fragments which contain the MS DNA.

To focus on and detect just the size and the number of DNA fragments in the sample which contain the MS DNA, a simple, yet powerful procedure is necessary. The steps in this "molecular fingerprinting" procedure are outlined in Figure 2.

First, the gel is treated with NaOH to denature the double-stranded DNA. This disrupts the hydrogen bonding between the complementary strands to produce single-stranded DNA.

After neutralization, the DNA is transferred to a filter paper which binds the single-stranded DNA. The filter retains the DNA fragments in the identical positions as that in the gel, but additionally places the DNA on the surface of the filter paper. Molecular biologists refer to this transfer procedure as a Southern blot.

To detect the specific bands which contain the MS DNA, a DNA fragment which is complementary to the MS DNA is radioactively labeled and then denatured to make a so-called single-strand DNA "probe".

The filter paper is then immersed in a solution containing the radioactive probe. The probe will hybridize to only complementary MS DNA sequences, which can then be detected by autoradiography.

Figure 3 shows the final results (autoradiogram) which would be observed for the DNA from three individuals (noted in Figure 1) and the DNA isolated directly from the hair found under the fingernail of the victim. DNA sample 2 was taken from the suspect, while samples 1 and 3 were from other individuals. You be the judge. Based on the DNA fingerprinting data, is the suspect guilty or innocent?

Figure 2   Detection Of MS DNA Using Southern Blotting

A human hair → Isolate DNA → Digest with Eco RI → Separate fragments by gel electrophoresis → Millions of bands appear as a smear → Transfer to Filter paper (Southern blot) → Hybridize with radioactively labeled minisatellite DNA → Autoradiogram

Bands for DNA fragments which hybridize to minisatellite DNA

Figure 3   Autoradiography For DNA Samples

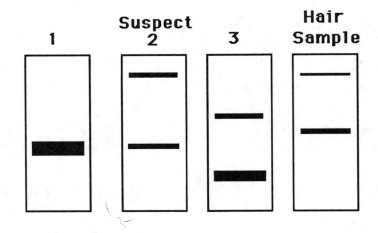

1   Suspect 2   3   Hair Sample

EXERCISES

1.   a.   Draw the structure for cytosine. What are the functional groups and the potential reactive sites in this pyrimidine base?

      b.   What are the smaller molecular components that make up a (ribo)nucleoside?

      c.   Name the nucleoside which has an adenine base.

      d.   What are the numbers for the positions in the bases and the sugar which are linked in (i) thymidine and (ii) guanosine and what is this linkage called?

      e.   What is the number for the ring atom in guanine which has a ketone group bonded to it?

      f.   Name the nucleoside derivative that has the abbreviation AZT. What is the parent nucleoside of this nucleoside? What is the modification introduced and at what position does it occur in the nucleoside?

2.   There are a variety of nucleotides which have different compositions and structures. Draw the structures for the following nucleotides:

      a.   5'-GDP

      b.   3'-dCMP

      c.   3', 5'-cAMP (cyclic AMP)

3.   a.   Why is the backbone in DNA or RNA referred to as a phosphodiester backbone?

      b.   Describe the structure for the tetranucleotide, pdCpdCpdGpdG, indicating the 5' and the 3' ends.

4.   a.   The original proposal for the structure of DNA was reported in 1953 by Watson and Crick. This structure was based on a collection of experimental data from many laboratories. One of the most important findings was the **fiber** diffraction data of Franklin and Wilkins. It is not possible from fiber diffraction data to determine the positions of individual atoms; this information simply had to be implied by effective model building. However, the data revealed a number of distinct distances in the DNA molecule. The

most important were 2 nm, 0.34 nm and 3.4 nm. What do these distances correspond to in the DNA molecule?

b.   Perplexing problems faced Watson and Crick as they attempted to build a model for the DNA molecule which was consistent with the data. The bases had to be positioned in a manner that was consistent with their hydrophobic character and arranged in a way that made both chemical and biological sense, together with being consistent with a diameter of 2.0 nm. Watson and Crick originally assumed that the G, C and T bases existed in the enol (-ene + -ol) tautomeric forms and not the keto forms. Draw the structures for the keto and enol tautomers for guanine.

c.   Draw the (guanosine-cytidine) base pair showing the hydrogen bonds between the bases.

d.   Examine both the (adenosine-thymidine) and the (guanosine-cytidine) base pairs. For the purine bases in each case, are the hydrogen bonds associated with atoms in the 5- or the 6-membered ring or both ring systems?

e.   If the guanine base were in the enol tautomeric form, would the Watson-Crick hydrogen bonding scheme in the GC base pair be possible?

5.   In the early 1980s, Wang and Rich reported the results of a single **crystal** X-ray diffraction study on the synthetic oligonucleotide, d(CGCGCG). This study provided for the first time, crystallographic data which specified the **atomic positions** in the DNA molecule. Data were finally available to support, modify or refute the long held structural proposal of Watson and Crick. The findings were both surprising and stunning! The structure confirmed the hydrogen bonding scheme that had been proposed by Watson and Crick for a (GC) base pair. However, the DNA exhibited a **left-handed helical twist**. This was the complete opposite to the twist proposed from the fiber diffraction patterns by Watson and Crick. This structural form of DNA was called **Z DNA**. In a very short time following this work, additional X-ray crystallographic studies on other DNAs verified the more common **B form** of DNA, which indeed did exhibit a **right-handed helical twist**.

Make a list of the structural characteristics of the Z form of DNA and compare these characteristics with those for the A and B forms of DNA.

6. Make a comparative list of differences between DNA and RNA.

7. What is a topoisomerase? What is the function of a topoisomerase in a cell?

8. A viral DNA isolated from monkeys contains 5,000 base pairs.

   a. If the DNA is in the B form, how many base pairs are there in each turn of the helical DNA?

   b. How many complete turns are expected in this DNA?

   c. If this DNA were ligated to make a covalently, closed, circular DNA, it is referred to as the "relaxed" form of DNA. Explain briefly.

   d. Consider that a topoisomerase cuts this relaxed form of DNA, 10 turns of the helix are removed (the DNA is unwound) and then the DNA is resealed.

      i. Is this a negatively or positively supercoiled DNA?

      ii. Is this a higher or lower energy form of DNA compared to the relaxed form? Explain briefly.

9. The histone proteins that are found in eukaryotic chromatin are some of the most highly conserved proteins known. This means that the amino acid sequence is virtually the same when these proteins are compared in species which diverged at very different times during evolution. Can you suggest a reason why these proteins remained virtually unchanged during millions of years of evolution?

10. There are two billion base pairs in human DNA. If it is assumed that (1) the nucleosome is associated with 200 base pairs of DNA and (2) that all the DNA in the nucleus of the cell is associated with nucleosomes, calculate the number of these repeating nucleosomes units which would be found in human chromatin.

11. a. Name the three different classes of RNA molecules.
    b. What is the function of each class of RNA?
    c. Which class of RNA molecule would be expected to be the most heterogeneous in size? Explain your reasoning.

12. a.　What is the difference between the specificity of an exonuclease and an endonuclease?

b.　There have been over 200 restriction endonucleases isolated and characterized. What property is common to all of these enzymes?

c.　A restriction endonuclease has the recognition sequence shown below.

GGCC

CCGG

The hydrolysis of the phosphodiester backbone occurs between the G and the C nucleotides in the middle of the recognition sequence.

How many smaller fragments of DNA would be produced if this restriction enzyme were added to a solution of each of the following DNA molecules? In each case, only one of the DNA strands is shown.

i.　　　GCGCATGGCATAGGGCCGGGAAATA

ii.　　ATATATGGGGGCATATCCCCGAGAG

iii.　　GCGCGGCCGGCCATGGCCATGCGGCG

13. a.　The Maxam-Gilbert method for sequencing DNA has been called the direct chemical method. Explain this briefly.

b.　Why did the discovery of restriction endonucleases permit DNA sequencing technology to develop?

c.　After the reaction of the radiolabeled DNA with chemicals and the subsequent cleavage at the modified nucleotides, what is the purpose of performing polyacrylamide gel electrophoresis on the labeled single-stranded DNA?

d.　What is the practical importance of radiolabeling the DNA and using autoradiography in the analysis of the DNA fragment sizes?

14. a.　In cloning technology, what is the difference between the vector and the recombinant DNA?

b.　Why is it convenient to cut both the vector and the DNA molecule to be cloned with the same restriction enzyme?

15. DNA can be denatured by increasing the temperature of the DNA solution.

a. What is the definition of T_m in a DNA denaturation experiment? This experiment is often referred to as a DNA "melting profile".

b. The melting profile for the same DNA was obtained under two different solution conditions. In one case, the NaCl concentration was 0.001 M, while the other condition was at 0.01 M NaCl. What effect would the different NaCl concentration have on the T_m value?

c. The alternating copolymer, poly d(GC). poly d(GC), can be converted from the B form of DNA to the Z form by a change in the salt concentration in the solution. It is known that the diameter of Z DNA is 1.8 nm, while that for the B form is 2.0 nm. Would you predict the Z form of DNA to exhibit a greater stability at a high or low salt concentration? Briefly explain your reasoning.

ANSWERS TO EXERCISES

1. a. The positions at which chemical reactions can occur in cytosine are the amine nitrogen atoms (1, 3 and the exocyclic amine), the ketone group at position 2 and the double bond between carbon atoms 5 and 6.

Cytosine (C)

b. A nucleoside is made up of a purine or pyrimidine base and a 5-membered cyclic sugar. The sugar in a ribonucleoside is a ribose.

c.   Adenosine

d.   In all nucleosides, the heterocyclic base is linked to the sugar at the C1' carbon atom. In a nucleoside containing a pyrimidine base (C, T or U), the N-1 atom in the base is bonded to the sugar. In the purine nucleosides (A or G), the N-9 atom is bonded to the sugar. In both cases, this carbon-nitrogen bond is called the β-glycosidic bond or linkage.

e.   The ketone group in guanine is at the C-6 position. Note that although the numbering system for both the purine and pyrimidine bases starts at a ring nitrogen, the nitrogen atom at which the numbering begins is different for the purine and pyrimidine base.

f.   AZT is the abbreviation for 3'-azido-3'-deoxythymidine. It is a modified thymidine nucleoside. An azide (N_3^-) group is linked to the C3' position of the deoxyribose sugar.

2a.

5'-GMP

b.

3'-dCMP

c.

3', 5'-cAMP

213

3. a.   The reaction of an acid with an alcohol produces an ester and water. Phosphoric acid is a triprotic, inorganic acid. Reaction with one alcohol group will produce a phosphate ester. Reaction with two alcohol groups, as is the case in DNA or RNA, produces a phosphate diester. This phosphodiester group is the repeating unit in the backbone of all nucleic acids.

$$H_3PO_4 \; + \; 2\,R\text{-}OH \; \xrightarrow{\hspace{1cm}} \; RO\text{-}\underset{\underset{O}{\|}}{\overset{\overset{O^-}{|}}{P}}\text{-}OR \; + \; 2\,H_2O$$

b.   The tetranucleotide, 5'-pdCpdCpdGpdG-3', is a small **deoxy**ribonucleotide, which has a phosphate group on the 5' end and an alcohol group on the 3' end. It is also an example of a self-associating oligonucleotide. If dissolved in solution, this single-stranded tetranucleotide can spontaneously form a double-stranded DNA.

Written out in an even more abbreviated form, the double-stranded DNA would be:

5' CCGG 3'
3' GGCC 5'

Note that this molecule exhibits a two-fold symmetry, which permits complementary base pairing in the formation of the double helix.

4. a.

Distance	Structural Characteristic
2 nm	the diameter of the double helical DNA
0.34 nm	the repeating distance between the base pairs along the major axis of DNA
3.4 nm	the repeating distance of one complete turn (10 base pairs) along the length of the DNA

b.

Keto-enol equilibrium for guanine, in
which the keto tautomer predominates.

c.

Complementary base pairing between
guanosine and cytosine (R= ribose).

d. In the Watson and Crick base-pairing scheme, the hydrogen bonds to or from the guanine (GC base pair) or adenine base (AT or AU base pair) are associated with the atoms in (only) the **six-membered** ring.

e. With the guanine in the enol form, the Watson-Crick base pairing scheme can not occur.

5.

Characteristic	Z DNA	B DNA	A DNA
Helical twist	left handed	right handed	right handed
Separation between bases	(0.37 nm)*	0.34 nm	(0.26 nm)
Anti-parallel strands	yes	yes	yes
Tilt to base pairs	slight	very slight	20^0 tilt
Number of base pairs/turn	(12)	10	11
Grooves on outside of DNA	barely detectable	very distinct	distinct
Diameter	(1.8 nm)	2.0 nm	(2.6 nm)

*- The values in parentheses are not presented in the text.

6.

	DNA	RNA
Strandedness	double	single
Functional participation	replication and transcription	transcription and translation
Composition		
Bases	A, T, G, C	A, U, G, C
Ribose	2'-deoxyribose	ribose
Location in cell	nucleus	nucleus, cytoplasm and within ribosomes

7.   A topoisomerase is a cellular enzyme which acts on a circular DNA substrate to change its level of supercoiling. This is accomplished by cutting the DNA backbone, either putting in an additional twist or taking one out and then resealing the backbone. When this action occurs, the resultant DNA is in a different topology and one topological isomer of DNA has been converted to another one (DNA with a different level of supercoiling). This explains the reason for the name and classification, topoisomerase, for the enzyme.

The function of a topoisomerase in the cell is to maintain the level of superhelicity in the DNA. It has been shown in a number of cases that replication, transcription and recombination processes are sensitive to the superhelicity of the DNA.

8.   a.   10 base pairs per turn
      b.   [5000 base pairs]/[10 base pairs per turn] = 500 helical turns
      c.   There is no additional stress or torsional forces on the DNA as a result of making the molecule circular.
      d.   i.   Negatively supercoiled DNA contains fewer turns than that found in the B form of DNA (490 turns < 500 turns). This is a negatively supercoiled DNA.
            ii.   This is a higher energy form because the removal of helical turns puts an additional stress on the DNA. This is apparent in that the DNA changes its tertiary structure to form additional turns in the form of supercoils to compensate for the stress.

9. The conservation or lack of change in the amino acid sequence in specific proteins throughout evolution is thought to be an indication of the essential role of the protein in processes vital to life. The histones are among the most highly conserved proteins known. They interact directly with DNA and form nucleosomes, which are the fundamental repeating subunits involved in the packaging of DNA and in the formation of chromatin structure in the nucleus. Any changes in the amino acid sequence must have an extremely detrimental effect on the packaging of DNA and therefore on the life of the cell.

10. Within the assumptions in the question, the number of nucleosomes in the nucleus of a human cell is:

$$[2.0 \times 10^{+9} \text{ base pairs}]/[2.0 \times 10^{+2} \text{ base pairs per nucleosome}] =$$

$$\underline{1.0 \times 10^{\pm 7} \text{ nucleosomes in human chromatin}}$$

11. a. There are three classes of RNA molecules:
    i. tRNA- transfer RNA
    ii. rRNA- ribosomal RNA
    iii. mRNA- messenger RNA

    b. Each tRNA molecule complexes with a specific amino acid at the 3' end of the tRNA and brings in an activated amino acid for the translational process on the ribosomes.
    Ribosomes are made up of rRNA molecules and a large number of proteins. These ribosomes provide the "stage" where protein synthesis takes place.
    The mRNA molecules are the molecular message carriers which take the genetic message to the ribosomes. The sequence of the mRNA therefore determines the composition and amino acid sequence of the protein to be synthesized.

    c. The most heterogeneous class of RNA is mRNA. There are a multitude of genes of widely varying sizes which are transcribed. The size of the gene will generally reflect the size of the protein which will be synthesized.

218

12.   a.   An exonuclease digests nucleic acids by the progressive hydrolysis of the terminal nucleotide. An endonuclease digests nucleic acids by hydrolyzing the backbone in the interior of the molecule.

b.   Each restriction endonuclease recognizes a specific sequence of double stranded DNA, binds to it and catalyzes the hydrolysis of the phosphodiester backbone at specific cut sites. The recognition sequence exhibits a two-fold symmetry and contains four or more base pairs.

c.   i.   There is only one GGCC recognition site in this molecule. Therefore, there is only one site for binding and subsequent hydrolysis. Two DNA fragments are produced, one with 10 base pairs and the other with 15 base pairs.

ii.   There are no GGCC recognition sites for this restriction endonuclease in this DNA. Therefore, there is no enzymatic cleavage and no smaller DNA fragments are produced.

iii.   Four DNA fragments are produced because there are three GGCC recognition sites. The DNA fragment sizes produced are 4, 6 and 10 base pairs. Note that two different DNA fragments are produced which have 6 base pairs.

13.   a.   The initial phase of the Maxam-Gilbert procedure involves **four individual reactions with the DNA. Each reaction selectively modifies either the G, A, C or T base on DNA.** As a result, the DNA backbone at each modified position is made very susceptible to hydrolysis. The distribution of fragments produced by the hydrolysis in each reaction will depend on the sequence of the original DNA.

b.   DNA sequencing is carried out on a distinct fragment of DNA which has a defined starting nucleotide and a terminal nucleotide. The hydrolysis of DNA with a restriction enzyme produces such fragments, as outlined in the previous problem.

c.   Polyacrylamide gel electrophoresis is used to separate and identify the size of the DNA fragments produced in each of the chemical modification reactions.

d.   Radiolabeling of the 5' end of the DNA with ^{32}P and the use of autoradiography provides a very sensitive method to detect very small quantities of DNA fragments.

14.   a.   A vector is a molecule of DNA to which the another DNA of interest is covalently inserted by ligation. The vector is often a bacterial plasmid or the DNA from a bacteriophage. Recombinant DNA is a DNA molecule which includes the vector DNA and the DNA fragment to be cloned.

b.   To clone a fragment of DNA into a vector, the DNAs must be ligated together to form a recombinant DNA. To carry this out, both the vector and the DNA may be cut with the same restriction endonuclease so each of the terminal ends has the same sequence. Generally, the restriction enzyme used will produce "sticky ends". When the resulting DNA fragments are mixed, the sticky ends from both fragments will associate with each other by complementary hydrogen bonding. DNA ligase is then added to ligate the backbone and produce the recombinant DNA.

15.   a.   The T_m value is the temperature at which the DNA is partially denatured and the absorbance is halfway between the final and starting absorbance values.

       b.   Increasing the salt concentration increases the stability of DNA and therefore also increases the value of the melting temperature. There are a number of forces which determine the stability of DNA. A force which tends to destabilize double stranded DNA is the repulsive force between the two DNA strands as a result of the negative phosphate units on each strand. The greater stability of DNA at a higher salt concentration results because the positively charged Na^+ ions will bind to the negatively charged phosphates on the DNA backbone and reduce the effective electrostatic repulsion of the interstrand phosphates.

       c.   The Z form of DNA has a smaller diameter. The interstrand phosphate units are closer to each other in Z DNA than in the B form DNA. At low salt concentration, the B form DNA will be more stable because of the smaller electrostatic repulsive forces between strands. The Z form would be expected to be more stable at a high salt concentration since this condition would favor a reduced electrostatic repulsion between the interstrand phosphates.

21

Biosynthesis of Nucleic Acids

DNA contains the genetic information in the form of a sequence of nucleotides. By the process of DNA replication, this information is passed on from one generation to the next with a remarkable fidelity. The DNA is synthesized in a continuous manner on the leading strand and in a discontinuous manner on the lagging strand of the replication fork. In *E. coli*, this is accomplished by a multitude of proteins and enzymes, including gyrase, helicase, single-strand DNA binding proteins, primase, DNA ligase and DNA polymerase III and I. Both of these DNA polymerases exhibit not only a polymerization activity, but also exonuclease activities to help attain a high fidelity in DNA replication. DNA is the only molecule in the cell which can be repaired if it is chemically or physically modified. The mechanisms for the repair of some types of DNA alterations are discussed, with the excision repair process for the removal of thymine dimers being one of the more thoroughly understood. Genetic recombination occurs during reproduction and increases our genetic diversity. This process requires homology between the strands of DNA and proceeds through a chi intermediate to generate a DNA with a different sequence. Transcription is the process of expressing the genetic material into RNA. All three forms of RNA undergo some degree of post-transcriptional processing. However, the most elaborate processing occurs on immature mRNA in eukaryotic cells. Both the 5' and 3' ends of mRNA become modified, the intron segments of the RNA are excised out and the exon segments spliced together.

CHAPTER OBJECTIVES

1.   Outline the role of nucleic acids in replication, transcription and translation.

2.   Discuss the experimental support for a semi-conservative mechanism of replication.

3.   Summarize the structure and the functional characteristics for *E. coli* DNA polymerase I, II and III.

4.   Identify the enzymatic activities of DNA polymerase I and III and indicate their role in DNA replication and DNA repair.

5.   List the proteins and enzymes associated with replication at the replication fork and indicate the function of each.

6.   Characterize the cut-and-patch process in the excision repair pathway that corrects chemically or physically altered segments of DNA.

7.   List the ways in which spontaneous and induced mutations of DNA can occur in a living cell.

8.   Discuss the mechanism for genetic recombination.

9.   Outline the characteristics of *E. coli* RNA polymerase and describe the steps in the synthesis of RNA.

10.   Describe the post-transcriptional processing that takes place on immature mRNA in the nucleus of the cell.

RNA as an Enzyme: The Changing of a Mind-Set

Transfer RNA (t-RNA) molecules play an essential role in the process of protein synthesis. Each t-RNA complexes with a specific amino acid, thereby activating it to the form utilized in protein synthesis.

t-RNA + amino acid ---> [t-RNA-amino acid]

However, prior to this step, a number of processing events must occur with high fidelity. The form of the t-RNA molecule produced initially in the nucleus (referred to as immature t-RNA), has additional segments of nucleotides on both its 5' and the 3' ends (solid black lines in the Figure below). These must be cleaved off to yield the mature t-RNA (shown as the thicker bands in the Figure).

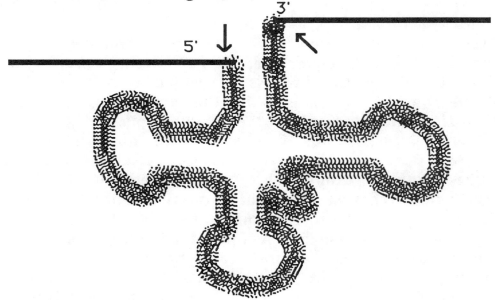

It had long been known that the enzyme which cleaves the 5' end of the immature t-RNA was the endonuclease, RNase P. This complex is composed of both a 14 kDa. protein and a 377-nucleotide RNA molecule. This remarkable enzyme correctly cleaves not only all 60 or so different t-RNAs in *E. coli*, but it can also carry out this processing event on precursor t-RNAs from other organisms. It was assumed that the protein was the catalyst, with the RNA possibly conferring stability and substrate specificity in the enzyme. Attempts to define the role of each subunit revealed that in physiological solution, containing 5-10 mM Mg^{+2}, the protein alone had no hydrolytic activity. Subsequent experiments examined the RNA and protein subunits separately and in all combinations for catalytic activity. The protein again exhibited no activity under any conditions. To the astonishment of Sidney Altman and his associates, the RNA alone showed activity in solution conditions in which the Mg^{+2} concentration was higher than normally used. To insure that there was no trace amounts of protein in the RNA sample, recombinant DNA techniques were used to prepare the pure RNA subunit of RNase P. This experiment showed this same activity and proved beyond any doubt that the RNA molecule exhibited the catalytic activity. The higher Mg^{+2} concentration that was required for activity of the lone RNA subunit suggested, and later it was shown to be the case, that the protein subunit in RNase P served in the complete enzyme (holoenzyme) as a "structural counter-ion" to provide stability. The enzyme obeys Michaelis-Menten kinetics with a K_M value of 5×10^{-7} M.

At this same time, Tom Cech's lab was studying the rRNA genes in the single cell eukaryote, *Tetrahymena thermophila*, and was intrigued by the process in which the intervening sequences (introns) were excised in the processing of the pre-rRNA. It was found that when the isolated pre-rRNA (containing the introns) was incubated with guanosine, in the absence of any protein, the intron excised itself and spliced together the flanking exons. This and subsequent studies showed that this reaction was autocatalytic, with the 413 nucleotide RNA being both the substrate and the catalyst, with a K_M value of 32 micromolar. A few other RNA molecules have since been shown to also exhibit catalytic activity.

With these findings in mind, it has now been suggested that RNA molecules may have been the original catalysts, but that they were restricted in the types of possible reactions they could catalyze due to the limited number of nucleotides in RNA. It is further speculated that during evolution, protein molecules, with twenty different amino acid residues to draw on for a very wide range of structures and activities, became the more versatile and numerous biological catalysts.

Sidney Altman and Tom Cech were awarded the Nobel Prize in Chemistry in 1989 for this seminal work which expanded the concept of enzymes and catalytic activity in biological molecules.

EXERCISES

1.   Describe two processes that can produce spontaneous mutations in DNA.

2.   Name three exogenous agents that can induce mutations in DNA.

3.   The enzyme uracil-DNA glycosidase participates in repair processes in *E. coli*.
      a.   What does it recognize in the DNA molecule?
      b.   What type of cleavage reaction does it catalyze?
      c.   What other enzymes are needed to complete the repair process?

4.   Draw a double-stranded DNA fragment which could be used as a template and primer for DNA synthesis by DNA polymerase I. Indicate the role of each strand in DNA synthesis.

5.   Arthur Kornberg isolated and characterized the first DNA polymerase from *E. coli* bacteria. A few years after this work on DNA polymerase I, a mutant form of *E. coli* was discovered that had the following characteristics:
      1.   The mutant bacteria had only 1% of the DNA polymerase I activity that was found in normal *E. coli* cells. However, cell division occurred at the same rate as in normal *E. coli* cells.

2.   The mutant *E. coli* cells were very sensitive to exposure to UV light, with a high percentage of the cells dying after irradiation.

What do these findings suggest about the possible function of DNA polymerase I in *E. coli* cells?

6.   Meselson and Stahl carried out a now classic density-gradient experiment in which they showed that DNA replication occurred by a semi-conservative mechanism.

Could the incorporation of ^{32}P and ^{31}P into the cells have worked equally well in these experiments as a replacement for ^{14}N and ^{15}N labeling? Explain briefly.

7.   a.   What precursor molecules are needed for DNA synthesis?

b.   In the formation of the phosphodiester backbone in DNA, what group on the DNA primer strand serves as the nucleophilic attacking group? What electrophilic group is the site of the attack? What are the products in this reaction?

c.   Is a high energy bond produced in the synthesis of DNA?

8.   Indicate the enzymatic activities associated with *E. coli* DNA polymerase I, II and III.

9.   Indicate the known cellular functions of *E. coli* DNA polymerase I, II and III.

10.   Indicate the role of the following proteins in DNA replication in *E. coli*.

a.   Gyrase
b.   DNA single-strand binding (SSB) proteins
c.   Helicase
d.   Primase
e.   DNA polymerase I
f.   DNA polymerase II
g.   DNA polymerase III

11. Thymine dimers are formed in DNA after irradiation with UV light. How many enzymes are known to participate in the repair of thymine dimers in *E. coli* and what are their roles in this process?

12. DNA polymerase I serves in primarily a repair role in *E. coli*, while polymerase III is the enzyme primarily responsible for DNA synthesis. What are the corresponding enzymes which carry out these functions in eukaryotes?

13. What is the difference in composition between the core and the holoenzyme for *E. coli* RNA polymerase? How does this relate to the functional roles of these two RNA polymerase complexes?

14. Indicate the three types of post-transcriptional modifications that are carried out on immature tRNA molecules.

15. Compare the structural gene, the corresponding immature mRNA transcript synthesized directly by RNA polymerase and the mature mRNA transcript which leaves the nucleus for translation in the cytoplasm of eukaryotes.

16. Indicate whether the following statements are true or false. If the statement is false, correct it.

     a.   All DNA polymerases synthesize DNA in a 5'---> 3' direction.

     b.   DNA synthesis requires a 5'-hydroxyl group on the primer strand.

     c.   Every "replication bubble" contains two replication forks.

     d.   Okazaki fragments are the RNA fragments in intron units.

     e.   Discontinuous DNA synthesis occurs on the leading strand of DNA.

     f.   *E. coli* DNA polymerase I is a more abundant protein in *E. coli* cells than is DNA polymerase III.

     g.   Sanger's method of sequencing DNA requires the use of 2',3'-dideoxyribonucleoside triphosphates.

     h.   DNA polymerase β in eukaryotic cells is thought to be a repair enzyme.

i.   One of the products of DNA recombination, referred to as the single-strand heterozygous product, contains two DNA molecules. Both of these DNA molecules have one DNA strand which is the same as the original, while the other strand contains parts of both original DNA strands.

j.   The rho protein is involved in the initiation of transcription by *E. coli* RNA polymerase.

ANSWERS TO EXERCISES

1.   Mutations can occur spontaneously during the process of replication and in the deamination of cytosine.

2.   Three exogenous agents which can cause mutations are UV radiation, X-rays and a large number of chemicals (mutagens).

3.   a.   Uracil-DNA glycosidase recognizes a uracil base in DNA.

b.   The enzyme cleaves the glycosidic bond between the uracil base and the deoxyribose. This leaves the DNA with an intact backbone, but with the base missing. This site is an **ap**yrimidinic site (i. e., one without a pyrimidine base).

c.   An endonuclease that recognizes apyrimidinic sites, the **AP** endonuclease, together with DNA polymerase I and DNA ligase are required to complete the repair process.

4.   The primer strand is the strand on which DNA synthesis occurs. It must have a terminal 3'-hydroxyl deoxyribose for synthesis to continue. The template strand is complementary to the primer strand. Therefore, the base on the template strand, because of its specific base pairing demands, determines the nucleotide which can be inserted in the primer strand.

Primer   3'-OH

T	G	C	T	C
A	C	G	A	G	T	T

Template

5.   The first observation suggested that DNA polymerase I was not the primary polymerase involved in DNA replication.

    The second observation suggested that DNA polymerase I might play a prominent role in the repair of UV damaged DNA.

6.   The isotopes, ^{32}P and ^{31}P, would be difficult or impossible to use in these experiments. The ^{14}N and ^{15}N isotopes are stable. Although the ^{31}P isotope is also stable, the ^{32}P isotope is radioactive and will decay rapidly. A less important reason is that there are more nitrogen atoms in DNA than there are phosphorus atoms.

7.   a.   DNA synthesis (i. e., DNA synthesis in vitro, or in a test tube) is a far simpler process than DNA replication (i. e., DNA synthesis in vivo or in a living organism). DNA synthesis requires a DNA primer (with a 3'-OH on the deoxyribose), a DNA template strand, Mg^{+2} ion, the four deoxyribonucleoside triphosphates and DNA polymerase.

    b.   The 3'-OH in the deoxyribose is the nucleophile that attacks the electrophilic phosphate group. The phosphate group is the one which is directly attached to the deoxyribose in the incoming nucleoside triphosphate. This phosphate, which forms the phosphodiester bond with the 3'-hydroxyl group, is the α-phosphate in the nucleoside triphosphate. The products of the reaction are DNA and pyrophosphate (P_iP_i).

    c.   The phosphate ester bond is a low energy bond.

8.   All three polymerases exhibit the 5' --> 3' polymerization and the 3' --> 5' exonuclease activities. DNA polymerase I and III also have the 5' --> 3' exonuclease activity, while polymerase II does not have this enzymatic capability.

9. DNA polymerase I is primarily involved in DNA repair. It also participates in DNA replication in which it digests the RNA primer fragments and then replaces them with the corresponding segment of DNA.

The function of DNA polymerase II is not known.

DNA polymerase III is the polymerase primarily responsible for DNA replication in *E. coli*.

10. a. Gyrase removes supercoils in front of the replication fork.

b. Single-strand binding proteins bind **preferentially** to single-stranded DNA. This stabilizes them so that replication can occur.

c. Helicase promotes unwinding of the DNA at the replication fork.

d. Primase synthesizes a small fragment of RNA which serves as a primer for DNA synthesis.

e. DNA polymerase I digests the RNA primer and synthesizes a DNA segment to fill the gap between the Okazaki fragments.

f. DNA polymerase II has no known function in replication.

g. DNA polymerase III synthesizes most of the DNA in the replication process.

11. The enzymes which participate in the excision repair of thymine dimers in *E. coli* are:

1. An endonuclease which nicks the phosphodiester backbone on both sides of the damaged region.

2. DNA polymerase I aids in the release of this damaged segment and synthesizes the correct DNA sequence to fill in this gap.

3. DNA ligase joins the newly synthesized segment to the DNA.

12. Eukaryotic DNA polymerase α is the primary polymerase in DNA replication, while DNA polymerase β, like DNA polymerase I in *E. coli*, is primarily involved in DNA repair.

13. The core RNA polymerase contains four subunits, $\alpha_2\beta\beta'$, and carries out chain elongation of the RNA in transcription. The RNA

polymerase holoenzyme, $\alpha_2\beta\beta'\sigma$, contains five subunits. The σ subunit is required for initiation of RNA synthesis at the correct nucleotide in DNA. The holoenzyme accomplishes this by binding to the promoter region of the gene. After initiation and during the elongation process, the σ subunit dissociates from the holoenzyme.

14. Immature tRNA molecules undergo trimming, addition of terminal sequences and the modification of some of the bases.

15. The structural gene is a segment of double-stranded DNA. The immature mRNA is an single strand of RNA complementary to one of the strands of DNA. The mature transcript undergoes a rather extensive post-transcriptional processing. This involves the capping of the 5' end of the transcript with a unique trinucleotide. A guanylate residue, which is methylated at the N-7 position, is added to the 5' end. This is attached to the adjacent ribose by a 5'-5' triphosphate linkage. Intron segments of the RNA are excised and the exons are spliced together. A polyadenylate "tail" is attached to the 3' end of the RNA to finish the mature RNA transcript. After this processing is completed in the nucleus, the mature transcript is transported into the cytoplasm for translation.

16.   a.   True.
       b.   False.   DNA synthesis requires a 3'-hydroxyl group on the primer strand.
       c.   True.
       d.   False.   Okazaki fragments are the small DNA fragments which are synthesized discontinuously on the lagging strand of the replication fork.
       e.   False.   Discontinuous DNA synthesis occurs on the lagging strand of the replication fork.
       f.   False.   DNA polymerase III is more abundant than DNA polymerase I in *E. coli.*.
       g.   True.
       h.   True.
       i.   True.
       j.   False.   The rho protein is involved in the termination of the RNA transcript in *E. coli.*

2 2

Biosynthesis of Proteins

Protein molecules are the "worker-bees" of the cell. Proteins and enzymes are essential to cellular metabolic activity and to the integrity of the cell itself. The biosynthesis of proteins is continuously taking place in all living cells and is one of the most complex of all cellular processes, with the participation of over 300 macromolecules. This intricate process begins with the activation of the amino acids to be incorporated into the protein. After the initiation of the protein chain, at what will become the amino end of the protein, individual amino acids are added to form peptide bonds in the growing peptide chain. Termination of protein synthesis results in the release of the protein from the ribosome and the dissociation of the entire protein synthesizing complex, including the ribosomes, mRNA, tRNAs and protein factors. The genetic message in the mRNA is translated into the sequence of amino acid residues in the protein according to the genetic code. These trinucleotide sequences in the mRNA form complementary hydrogen bonds with the anticodon triplets in the activated tRNA molecules. The primary regulation of gene expression in prokaryotes occurs at the level of transcription and is generally described by the operon theory. The lactose operon is a paradigm for the understanding of the expression of other genes in prokaryotic organisms.

CHAPTER OBJECTIVES

1. Explain the roles of mRNA, tRNAs and rRNAs in the translation process.
2. Describe the most important features of amino acid activation, chain initiation, chain elongation and chain termination in the synthesis of a protein.
3. Indicate the enzymes and their roles in the process of protein synthesis.
4. Describe the experiments which were carried out to decipher the genetic code.
5. Explain the importance of the codon-anticodon interaction between mRNA and tRNA and the "wobble" hypothesis.
6. Discuss the general differences between translation in prokaryotes and eukaryotes.
7. Describe the major features of the operon theory of gene expression in prokaryotes as it relates to the lactose operon.
8. Outline the molecular and cellular features of the immune response in vertebrates.

SPOTLIGHT

Cystic Fibrosis:
The Gene, The Protein and Possible Gene Therapy

Cystic fibrosis (CF) is the most common lethal congenital disease in Caucasians. While one in every 20 individuals is a carrier, the incidence is 1 in 2,000 live births, with estimates that about 5,000 individuals die each year from CF. CF is a disease of the secretory epithelia. The cells in this tissue mediate transport of primarily water and salt from the blood to the outside world (i.e., the lumen). The clinical manifestations observed in afflicted individuals are the decrease in the secretion of fluid and the accumulation of a thick mucus in the bronchial tubes. This blocks the airways, promotes bacterial infections and after years of chronic lung infections, leads to heart and lung failure.

1989 was a momentous year for biomedical research into CF in that the gene associated with CF was cloned. It is located on chromosome 7, spans 250 kilobases of DNA and has 24 exons. On comparison of the gene from normal individuals with those with CF, it was found that about 70% of the CF patients had three bases missing (only 3 adjacent bases of the 250,000 bases in the gene!). This leads to 3 bases missing in the mRNA and, since this corresponded to a codon - the codon for phenylalanine - the CF protein had this single amino acid residue deleted at position 508 in this protein of 1,480 amino acid residues. A number of pieces of data, including the structure, clearly indicated to membrane biologists that it was a membrane protein. It was called the Cystic Fibrosis Transmembrane Regulator (CFTR). The CF gene is only expressed (i.e., transcribed and translated into protein) in certain cells, with the tissues being the pancreas, the sweat glands and the lining of the respiratory tract. Consistent with this gene being associated with CF, these are the tissues in which the disease manifests itself. Previous findings had also indicated that the disease was not associated with the absence

234

of chloride ion channels, but with the _abnormal regulation_ of the channels.

The accompanying Figure shows a tentative model for the CFTR in association with the membrane. The protein passes through the membrane (12 times), with both the amino- and carboxyl-ends of the protein being in the cytoplasm, together with a region of the protein which has binding domains for ATP. This suggests that the protein may act as an ion pump, rather than a simple ion channel. Note that the mutation is near the ATP binding domains.

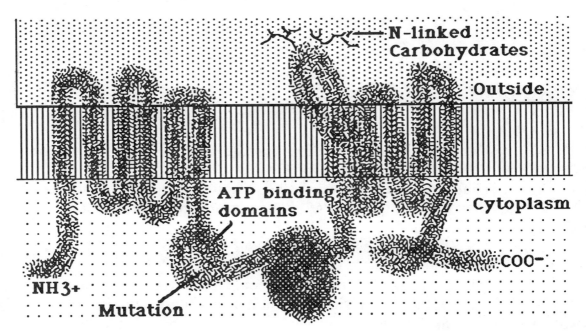

Knowing the molecular culprit which appears responsible for the disease is a giant step in understanding CF, but it can be very far from providing an effective treatment for the disease. However, in September of 1990, stunning experiments were successfully performed on cells in culture which showed the following:

1. The _normal_ CF gene was inserted into cells which had a defective CF gene and therefore faulty CFTRs (clogged chloride ion channels). After the cells took up the gene, normal CFTRs were produced and the chloride ion channels were opened. This showed that insertion of a normal gene into a living cell could be expressed to produce a physiologically significant change in the cell.

2. This experimental finding also provided indisputable evidence that the isolated gene is, in fact, the cystic fibrosis gene and its protein product is a chloride ion channel protein.

The future appears very exciting. Experiments are being planned on an animal model for cystic fibrosis, with a number of mechanisms being considered in which the gene may be effectively inserted into the epithelial cells in the airways of the animal. An aerosol spray has been discussed as a possible delivery system.

EXERCISES

1   a.   Write the overall reaction for the activation of an amino acid.

      b.   What enzyme catalyzes this reaction?

      c.   How many high energy bonds are hydrolyzed in the activation process?

2.   a.   Which end of the tRNA molecule binds to the amino acid?

      b.   Specify the exact site at which the amino acid is covalently bound to the tRNA molecule and the type of chemical linkage produced by the reaction.

3.   a.   What are the sizes of the subunits (in Svedberg units, S values) that make up the ribosome in *E. coli*? What is the size of the complete ribosome?

      b.   Describe the two types of interactions between the mRNA and the 16S rRNA in the small ribosomal subunit that determine where protein synthesis starts.

      c.   Which ends of the mRNA and the 16S rRNA molecules act as the starting point for the translation process?

      d.   Describe the composition of the Shine-Dalgarno sequence. Which RNA does this sequence reside on and where is its relative location in the RNA?

      e.   What is the DNA sequence that corresponds to the Shine-Dalgarno sequence?

4.   a.   DNA is synthesized in what direction?

        b.   DNA is read by DNA polymerase in what direction?

        c.   RNA is synthesized in what direction?

        d.   DNA is read by RNA polymerase in what direction?

        e.   Protein synthesis begins at what end of the mRNA molecule?

        f.   What is the orientation of the anticodon triplet in tRNA relative to the codon sequence on mRNA?

        g.   Which end of the protein is synthesized first?

5.   In prokaryotic organisms, translation occurs before the mRNA is completed, but this does not occur in eukaryotic cells. Explain briefly.

6.   a.   Define the term genetic code.

        b.   Synthetic RNA polynucleotides were used to help define the nucleotide triplets on mRNA which corresponded to the amino acids to be incorporated in proteins. What proteins are produced by the translation of the following RNA molecules?

        i.   poly(UUU)

        ii.   poly(GCA)

        iii.   poly(AU)

7.   a.   What is the relative orientation of the codon and anticodon triplets as they base pair with each other?

        b.   What is the "wobble" hypothesis?

8.   The first 15 nucleotides in the DNA sequence of a gene is GGACCAGTCACACAT-. This is the DNA strand that is read by RNA polymerase. What is the corresponding amino acid sequence?

9.   The protein that is coded for by the gene associated with the disease cystic fibrosis is 155.4 kDa. in size (considering only the amino acid residues). It is estimated that the rate of protein synthesis is about 15 amino acid residues/sec. Calculate the time needed to complete the synthesis of this protein.

10.   a.   Indicate the operon terms which have the abbreviations I, P, O, Z, Y and A.
   b.   What is the order of these regions in the operon DNA?
   c.   Indicate what effect a defective mutation (e.g., a premature stop codon or one that would alter the binding of a regulator protein to the DNA sequence) in each of the following regions would have on the expression of the structural genes.
   i.   I region
   ii.   O region
   iii.   P region

11.   Indicate whether the following statements are true or false. If the statement is false, correct it.

   a.   The minimum number of adjacent nucleotides in mRNA that can define the genetic code is three.
   b.   In *E. coli*, the tRNA^{fmet} combines with N-formylmethionine to form the initial amino acid in the synthesis of a protein.
   c.   The initiation of translation in *E. coli* requires the formation of a complete ribosome.
   d.   Translocation is the movement of the peptidyl-tRNA from the P site to the A binding site.
   e.   Puromycin blocks translation by inhibiting the enzyme peptidyl transferase.
   f.   The only amino acids which have unique codons are methionine and tryptophan.
   g.   The binding of CAP-cAMP to the promoter site in the lac operon inhibits the expression of the lac structural genes.
   h.   The B cells manufacture antibodies and act in concert with a variety of T cells to mount an immune response in vertebrates.

238

ANSWERS TO EXERCISES

1.   a.   amino acid + ATP + tRNA ---> aminoacyl-tRNA + PP_i

      b.   Aminoacyl-tRNA synthetase catalyzes this reaction.

      c.   There are two high energy bonds hydrolyzed in this process. ATP is hydrolyzed to yield AMP + PP_i. The PPi is then hydrolyzed to two phosphates.

2   a.   The amino acid binds to the 3' end of the tRNA.
      b.   The reaction occurs at the 3'-hydroxyl group of the ribose ring of adenosine. Recall that one of the common features in all tRNA molecules is that the last three nucleotides at the 3' end are CpCpA.
      The amino acid-tRNA linkage formed is an ester bond (refer to Figure 22.2 in the text).

3   a.   In *E. coli*, the ribosomal subunits are 30S and 50S, with the complete ribosome having an S value of 70.
      b.   Two types of hydrogen bonding interactions determine the start point for protein synthesis. The mRNA interacts with the Shine-Dalgarno sequence in the 3' end of the 16S rRNA and the anticodon sequence of the initiator tRNA[fmet] interacts with the start codon on mRNA.
      c.   The 5' end of the mRNA interacts with the 3' end of the 16S rRNA.
      d.   The Shine-Dalgarno sequence is the purine-rich sequence, 5'-GGAGGU-3'. It resides on the 5' end of the mRNA, about 10 nucleotides upstream from the initiator codon.
      e.   The corresponding pyrimidine-rich DNA sequence is 5'-ACCTCC-3'.

4.   a.   DNA is synthesized in the 5' ---> 3' direction.
     b.   The DNA strand is read by DNA polymerase in the 3' ---> 5' direction.
     c.   RNA is synthesized in the 5' ---> 3' direction.
     d.   The DNA strand that is read by RNA polymerase is in the 3' ---> 5' direction.
     e.   Protein synthesis begins at the 5' end of the mRNA molecule.
     f.   The codon and anticodon triplets are oriented in an antiparallel alignment, with complementary base pairs between the mRNA and the tRNA molecules.
     g.   The amino end of the protein is synthesized first.

5.   There are no organelles in prokaryotic organisms. Both transcription and translation occur in the cytoplasm. Therefore, after only a small segment of the mRNA has been synthesized, translation can begin immediately.

     In eukaryotic cells, transcription occurs in the nucleus, while translation occurs on the ribosomes in the cytoplasm. The immature mRNA undergoes extensive processing before it leaves the nucleus and is transported to the cytoplasm for protein synthesis. Only after the mRNA interacts with the ribosomes in the cytoplasm can translation begin. Therefore, transcription and translation are separated both spacially and temporally in eukaryotic cells.

6.   a.   Translation is the process of synthesizing proteins from the instructions in the genetic material. The molecular messenger that brings the instructions from DNA to the cytoplasm is mRNA. This is the point at which the "nucleotide alphabet" is converted to the "amino acid alphabet" and the molecular communications problem, dealing with two different languages, must be resolved. The nucleotide alphabet has four letters, while the amino acid alphabet has twenty letters. The genetic code is the direct correspondence between these two languages. A triplet of adjacent nucleotides in mRNA defines an amino acid to be incorporated into a protein.

b.   i.   Protein synthesis with poly(UUU) serving as the mRNA will produce a homopolypeptide with only phenylalanine residues in it {i.e., poly(phenylalanine)}.

ii.   Translation using poly(GCA) as the mRNA will also produce a homopolypeptide, polyalanine. This result is consistent with the genetic code being made up of triplets of nucleotides.

iii.   Translation with poly(AU) will produce a heteropolypeptide. This occurs since the genetic code involves a triplet of nucleotides. Therefore, the message in poly(AU) will be a repeating unit of AUA and UAU triplets - **AUAUAUAUAUAUAUAU**...

This will produce poly(ile-tyr).

7.   a.   The codon is read in a 5' --->3' direction in mRNA. The codon-anticodon interact by antiparallel strands, with the anticodon in a 3' ---> 5' direction. The two triplets interact through Watson-Crick base pairing.

b.   The "wobble" hypothesis refers to observation that the base at the 5' end of the anticodon has less restrictions on the base pairs it may form. The other two bases in the anticodon are restricted to engaging in only Watson-Crick base pairing with the bases in the codon triplet.

8.   DNA   5'-**GGACCAGTCACACAT**-3'

mRNA   5'-**AUGUGUGACUGGUCC**-3'
Alternating triplets are shown in bold type for easier reading.

protein $+H_3N$-met-cys-asp-trp-ser---

9.   Assume the average molecular weight of an amino acid residue is ca. 105 Da. The number of amino acid residues in this protein would be 155,400/105 = 1480. At a rate of translation of 15 residues/sec, it would require only about 99 seconds or slightly longer than a minute and one-half to synthesize this enormous protein.

10. a.   The abbreviations are for the following operon terms:
                    I- the regulatory gene,
                    P- the promoter region,
                    O- the operator region,
                    Z, Y and A- the structural genes.
     The I, P and O regions are upstream from the structural genes and control the expression of these genes into RNA and the protein products.
     b.   The order of the operon elements, from the 5' end to the 3' end of the DNA, is I, P, O, followed by the structural genes, Z, Y and A.
     c.   i.   A mutation that produces a premature stop codon results in a nonfunctioning protein product. A mutation in I would result in an incomplete repressor molecule being synthesized. If there were no functional repressor available to bind to the operator, synthesis would be continuously turned on.
            ii.   The operator sequence does not code for a protein. A mutation in the operator would alter the binding of the repressor protein to the operator sequence. If the binding interaction were weaker as a result of the mutation, RNA polymerase might be able to "compete the repressor off" the operator sequence and carry out transcription. This would result in an increase of transcription to some degree.
            iii.   The promoter sequence does not code for a protein. A mutation in the promoter sequence will alter the extent that RNA polymerase binds to it. If the mutation weakens this interaction, this may result in a decrease in the level of transcription.

11. a.   True.
     b.   False.   The t-RNA^{fmet} combines with methionine, which is subsequently modified to produce N-formylmethionine.
     c.   True.
     d.   False.   The movement is from the A binding site to the P site.
     e.   False.   Puromycin blocks translation by either (1) binding to the P site and blocking translocation or (2) being incorporated into the peptide at the carboxyl end of the growing peptide chain. The peptidyl-puromycin then dissociates from the ribosome as a prematurely terminated protein.
     f.   True.

g. False. The CAP-cAMP complex must bind to the promoter site for transcription to occur.

h. True.